EOE ELIMINATION DIET COOKBOOK

The Kids and Beginners Guide with Six Allergens- Recipes, Meal Plan, and Preps for the Empiric, Reintroduction, and Maintenance Phases for Eosinophilic Esophagitis "

Amos jimmy

TABLE OF CONTENT

INTRODUCTION

Welcome to the "EOE Elimination Diet Cookbook," your comprehensive guide to navigating the challenging yet rewarding journey toward managing Eosinophilic Esophagitis (EOE) through dietary changes. This cookbook is designed to be your companion from the very beginning of your diet modification journey, offering support and guidance through each critical phase: the Empiric Elimination Diet, the Reintroduction Phase, and finally, the Maintenance Phase.

The Empiric Elimination Diet phase is where your journey begins. We understand the overwhelm and confusion that can come with identifying which foods to avoid to manage your EOE symptoms. This section of the book is meticulously crafted to ease you into the elimination diet with a selection of delicious, safe recipes that exclude common triggers. Our goal is to ensure that, despite the restrictions, your meals remain nutritious, satisfying, and enjoyable.

The Reintroduction Phase is a critical period of discovery and understanding. It's the phase where you start to reintroduce foods back into your diet, one at a time, to identify potential allergens. This can be a time of uncertainty, but our cookbook provides structured guidance to help you navigate this phase confidently. You'll find recipes that are tailored for the reintroduction of specific foods, allowing you to monitor your symptoms accurately and make informed decisions about your diet.

The Maintenance Phase is where you establish a long-term diet that maintains the balance between managing EOE and enjoying a broad, varied diet. This section offers recipes that are flexible and adaptable, allowing you to incorporate the foods you've successfully reintroduced while avoiding those that exacerbate your symptoms. Our recipes aim to inspire creativity and variety in your diet, ensuring that you feel satisfied and fulfilled.

Throughout this cookbook, you'll find not just recipes, but also insights into managing EOE, tips for meal planning, and advice for living a balanced life despite dietary restrictions. Whether you're newly diagnosed, a long-term EOE manager, or cooking for someone with EOE, this cookbook is designed to support you at every stage of your dietary journey.

CHAPTER 1

UNDERSTANDING EOE ELIMINATION DIET

Eosinophilic Esophagitis (EoE) is a chronic, immune-mediated or allergic condition where eosinophils (a type of white blood cell) accumulate in the esophagus, the tube that carries food from the mouth to the stomach.

This accumulation causes inflammation and can lead to various gastrointestinal symptoms such as difficulty swallowing (dysphagia), food impaction, chest pain, and heartburn.

The treatment for EoE often involves dietary management, medication, and, in some cases, dilation of the esophagus. One crucial aspect of managing EoE through diet involves entering a maintenance phase after the initial treatment phase has effectively reduced symptoms and inflammation.

Understanding Elimination Diets

An elimination diet is a method used to identify foods that an individual may be allergic or sensitive to. By removing certain foods from the diet and then gradually reintroducing them, one can pinpoint specific triggers of allergic reactions or symptoms. This approach is particularly useful in managing EoE, as certain foods can exacerbate the condition. The goal is to achieve symptom relief and a decrease in eosinophil counts in the esophagus while maintaining a nutritionally balanced diet.

The Empiric Elimination Diet

The Empiric Elimination Diet involves removing the most common allergens from the diet. These typically include **milk, eggs, wheat, soy, peanuts/tree nuts, and fish/shellfish.** This approach is based on the premise that the majority of food-related allergic reactions are caused by a relatively small number of foods. By eliminating these common allergens, individuals with EoE may see a significant reduction in symptoms and esophageal eosinophilia.

The process begins with the total removal of these six food groups from the diet for a period, typically ranging from **six to eight weeks.**

This phase requires careful planning and dietary adjustments to ensure nutritional needs are met despite the restrictions. After the elimination phase, foods are reintroduced one at a time, with a period of observation between each reintroduction to monitor for symptoms or reactions. This stepwise reintroduction helps identify specific foods that trigger EoE symptoms, allowing for a personalized diet plan that avoids these triggers while being less restrictive overall.

The Step-Up Approach

The Step-Up Approach to dietary management in EoE offers an alternative to the broad restrictions of the Empiric Elimination Diet. This method starts with a less restrictive diet, eliminating only one or two of the most common allergens initially. If symptoms do not improve, additional foods are progressively eliminated from the diet until symptom relief is achieved.

This approach can be less daunting for patients, as it allows for a more gradual adjustment to dietary changes. It also minimizes the risk of nutritional deficiencies by maintaining a broader range of food options from the start. However, the Step-Up Approach may require more time to identify all of the individual's food triggers, as the process of adding and removing foods is more gradual.

Implementing Elimination Diets: Challenges and Considerations

While elimination diets are effective in managing EoE, they come with their own set of challenges. Strict adherence to the diet is crucial for its success, which can be difficult, especially in social settings or when eating out. Furthermore, the risk of nutritional deficiencies is heightened, particularly with the Empiric Elimination Diet, due to the broad range of foods eliminated. Working with a dietitian is essential to ensure that the diet remains balanced and that any nutritional gaps are addressed through appropriate supplementation or dietary adjustments.

It's also important to recognize the emotional and psychological impact of such dietary restrictions. Feelings of isolation, frustration, and food anxiety are common among individuals following strict elimination diets. Support from healthcare providers, family, and peer support groups can be invaluable in navigating these challenges.

The reintroduction stage

The Strategic Approach to Reintroduction and Food Selection in EoE Management

Managing Eosinophilic Esophagitis (EoE) through dietary interventions is a nuanced process, central to which is the reintroduction phase. This phase is pivotal, not only for identifying specific food triggers but also for crafting a diet that is both satisfying and nutritionally complete, devoid of unnecessary restrictions. Here, we dissect the strategic approach to food reintroduction and delve into considerations for selecting foods to reintroduce to patients with EoE.

Strategic Approach to Reintroduction

The reintroduction phase is approached with a methodical and patient-centric strategy, ensuring the identification of food triggers while maintaining nutritional adequacy and quality of life. This phase is characterized by several key steps:

Comprehensive Assessment and Preparation: Prior to reintroduction, a thorough evaluation of the patient's clinical status is essential. This involves confirming the remission of EoE symptoms and possibly conducting an endoscopy to verify esophageal healing. Such assessments set the stage for a safe and effective reintroduction phase.

Prioritizing Foods for Reintroduction: The selection of foods for reintroduction is critical and should be strategically prioritized based on several factors, including the nutritional value of the food, its commonality in triggering EoE, and the patient's personal preference and dietary habits. This personalized approach ensures that the diet remains balanced and culturally relevant to the patient.

Structured and Phased Reintroduction: Foods are reintroduced sequentially, one at a time, with a typical trial period lasting 2-4 weeks for each food. This controlled approach allows for the clear identification of culprits that exacerbate symptoms. Patient education on symptom tracking and the use of food diaries is crucial during this phase.

Evaluation and Monitoring: Continuous monitoring and evaluation are imperative throughout the reintroduction phase. Patients are advised to keep detailed records of their dietary intake and any subsequent symptoms. Regular follow-ups with healthcare professionals facilitate timely adjustments to the reintroduction plan.

Collaborative Decision-Making: Decisions regarding the reintroduction process are made collaboratively, involving input from the patient, dietitians, and physicians. This team approach ensures that all aspects of the patient's health and well-being are considered.

Selecting Foods for Reintroduction

The selection of foods for reintroduction is a critical element of the strategic approach, requiring careful consideration of several factors:

Nutritional Value: Foods with high nutritional value are prioritized to ensure that the diet remains balanced and supports overall health. This includes foods rich in vitamins, minerals, fiber, and other essential nutrients.

Commonality of EoE Triggers: Foods less commonly associated with EoE symptoms are often reintroduced first. This strategy aims to expand the diet as broadly as possible while minimizing the risk of symptom recurrence. Common allergens, such as dairy, eggs, soy, wheat, nuts, and seafood, are typically reintroduced later in the process.

Patient Preference and Dietary Habits: Incorporating the patient's preferences and cultural dietary practices into the selection process is vital for ensuring adherence and satisfaction with the diet. Foods that hold cultural significance or are particularly favored by the patient can be prioritized, within the constraints of their potential to trigger EoE symptoms.

Diversity of the Diet: To prevent nutritional deficiencies and ensure a pleasurable eating experience, a diverse range of foods is considered for reintroduction. This not only enhances the nutritional quality of the diet but also improves adherence by offering variety and preventing monotony.

Reorganizing the six common allergens from least likely to most likely

Reorganizing the six common allergens from least likely to most likely to be reintroduced based on their potential allergenicity and offering substitutions for each provides a strategic approach for managing EoE while maintaining nutritional balance.

Here's the list in ascending order of reintroduction potential, along with substitutions to ensure nutritional adequacy:

Fish/Shellfish (Most Likely for Early Reintroduction)

Nutritional Value: High in omega-3 fatty acids, proteins, vitamins D and B2 (riboflavin), calcium, minerals, including iron, zinc, iodine, magnesium, and potassium.

Reintroduction Consideration: Fish and shellfish are less commonly reported as triggers for EoE compared to other allergens like milk or wheat. Due to their high nutritional value, especially omega-3 fatty acids which have anti-inflammatory properties, reintroducing fish early might be beneficial for individuals unless specifically known to trigger symptoms.

Substitutions:

- For omega-3 fatty acids, flaxseeds, chia seeds, and walnuts are excellent plant-based sources.
- Plant-based protein sources or other meats (if not allergic) can replace the protein contribution of fish and shellfish.

Eggs

Nutritional Value: Excellent source of high-quality protein, vitamins A, D, E, K, B vitamins, and minerals such as zinc, iron, and selenium.

Reintroduction Consideration: Eggs are a versatile food, but they are also a common allergen. When reintroducing eggs, it's advisable to start with baked egg products, as cooking can alter the allergenicity of egg proteins, making them less likely to cause a reaction.

Substitutions:

- Chia or flax seeds mixed with water can create a gel-like substitute for eggs in baking.
- Commercial egg replacers are available that provide similar binding properties without the allergenic components.

Milk

Nutritional Value: Good source of calcium, vitamin D, and protein; essential for bone health and muscle function.

Reintroduction Consideration: Dairy is a significant allergen for many with EoE, but its nutritional benefits, particularly for bone health, are substantial. Consider reintroducing dairy products that are fermented or lower in lactose, such as kefir or hard cheeses, which may be better tolerated and can help gauge sensitivity.

Substitutions:

- Plant-based milks (almond milk, oat milk) offer alternatives rich in vitamins and minerals.
- Calcium-fortified foods and beverages can help maintain calcium intake in the absence of dairy.

Wheat

Nutritional Value: Source of fiber, B vitamins, and minerals such as iron, magnesium, and zinc.

Reintroduction Consideration: Wheat, particularly whole wheat, is valuable for its fiber and nutrient content. When reintroducing wheat, starting with small amounts of gluten-containing grains might help identify tolerance levels.

Consider whole wheat products for their additional nutritional benefits.

Substitutions:

- Gluten-free grains (quinoa, rice, buckwheat) are excellent alternatives to wheat and provide a variety of nutrients along with being good sources of carbohydrates and fiber.
- Almond flour or coconut flour can serve as a gluten-free baking alternative.

Soy

Nutritional Value: Contains protein, isoflavones, fiber, and omega-3 fatty acids. It's a good plant-based protein source, particularly for vegetarians and vegans.

Reintroduction Consideration: Soy can be introduced by starting with foods that contain smaller amounts of soy protein, like soy oil or soy lecithin, to test tolerance. Moving to more significant sources, such as tofu or soy milk, can help determine if soy is a trigger.

Substitutions:

- Legumes (lentils, chickpeas) provide protein and fiber, serving as a good alternative to soy-based proteins.
- Almond milk or coconut milk can replace soy milk for those avoiding soy.

Peanuts/Tree Nuts (Least Likely for Early Reintroduction)

Nutritional Value: Nuts are a good source of protein, healthy fats (particularly omega-6 and omega-3 fatty acids), vitamin E, and minerals like magnesium and phosphorus.

Reintroduction Consideration: Given the high nutritional value and the fact that not all nuts will necessarily trigger symptoms, reintroducing nuts individually can help identify specific nuts that are safe. Starting with nuts that are less allergenic, such as almonds or cashews, might be advisable before introducing more commonly allergenic nuts like peanuts.

Substitutions:

- Seeds (sunflower, pumpkin) can be a good alternative for nuts in terms of providing healthy fats, proteins, and minerals.

- Seed butters (such as sunflower butter) offer a nut butter alternative for those avoiding peanuts/tree nuts.

Implementing the Reintroduction Phase

Implementation of the reintroduction phase is marked by patience and precision. Each reintroduced food undergoes a trial period, during which patients are closely monitored for any signs of symptom recurrence. Positive and negative outcomes of these trials guide further reintroductions, with the goal of crafting a personalized diet that minimizes restrictions while effectively managing EoE symptoms.

For instances where symptoms recur upon reintroduction of a specific food, it is labeled as a trigger and excluded from the diet. Conversely, foods that do not elicit symptoms are gradually incorporated into the patient's regular diet, expanding their dietary options and improving quality of life.

In the reintroduction stage we will add only 2 allergen ingredient

WHICH ARE EGGS AND MILK WITH THE SUBSTITUTION IF IT TRIGGERS

The maintenance phase

Transitioning to the Maintenance Phase

Once the inflammation is under control and symptoms have significantly reduced or disappeared, the individual transitions into the maintenance phase of the diet. The primary goal of this phase is to maintain symptom control and esophageal health while reintroducing more foods to the diet, making the diet more varied and nutritionally balanced.

Steps in the Maintenance Phase

Reintroduction of Foods: This involves gradually reintroducing foods that were previously eliminated, one at a time, to identify any that might trigger symptoms. The patient is closely monitored for any signs of EoE flare-ups. If a food does not cause symptoms, it can be permanently added back into the diet. This step requires careful planning and coordination with a healthcare provider, typically a dietitian or an allergist.

Monitoring and Adjusting: Regular follow-ups are crucial during this phase. These appointments are used to assess the patient's response to the reintroduced foods and adjust the diet as needed. This might involve removing a food that has been identified as a new trigger or trying to reintroduce a food that previously caused symptoms, to see if tolerance has developed over time.

Education and Support: Patients and their families receive education on reading food labels, understanding cross-contamination risks, and preparing foods to prevent accidental exposure to allergens. Support groups or counseling may also be helpful during this time, as dietary restrictions can significantly impact one's lifestyle and emotional well-being.

Long-term Dietary Management: The maintenance phase is essentially a long-term dietary management strategy. It's about finding a balance between avoiding triggers and maintaining a healthy, satisfying diet. This balance is crucial for preventing malnutrition and ensuring quality of life.

Dealing with Flare-ups: Even with careful management, EoE flare-ups can occur. Patients learn to recognize the early signs of a flare-up and understand how to adjust their diet temporarily to manage symptoms.

Challenges and Considerations

The maintenance phase is not without its challenges. It requires the patient to be vigilant about their diet and symptoms, and there can be frustration over the trial and error process of reintroducing foods. Additionally, the risk of developing new food sensitivities exists, requiring adjustments to the diet.

Furthermore, the emotional and social impact of dietary restrictions can be significant. Patients may feel isolated during social events centered around food or overwhelmed by the need for constant vigilance. Psychological support and finding a supportive community can play a critical role in managing these challenges.

CHAPTER 2

BREAKFAST RECIPES

EMPIRIC ELIMINATION DIET

Quinoa Breakfast Bowl

Serves: 1

Cooking Time: 20 minutes

Ingredients and Portions/Measurements:

- Quinoa: 1/2 cup (A complete protein source, gluten-free and EoE elimination diet-friendly)
- Water: 1 cup (For cooking quinoa, no nutritional impact but essential for hydration)
- Chia Seeds: 1 tablespoon (Rich in omega-3 fatty acids, fiber, and tolerated by most on an elimination diet; Substitute: Flaxseeds [1 tablespoon])
- Sliced Banana: 1/2 banana (Provides natural sweetness and potassium; Phase 1 Elimination EoE diet-friendly)

- Cinnamon: A pinch (Adds flavor without calories or allergens; Phase 1 Elimination EoE diet-friendly)
- Unsweetened Almond Milk: 1/4 cup (Optional for creaminess, ensure it's free of additives for EoE diet; Substitute: Coconut Milk [1/4 cup] if tolerated)

Instructions:

- Rinse quinoa under cold water. In a small pot, bring 1 cup of water to a boil. Add quinoa, reduce heat to low, cover, and simmer for 15 minutes or until all water is absorbed.
- Remove from heat and let it sit, covered, for 5 minutes. Fluff quinoa with a fork.
- While quinoa is cooking, prepare your toppings.
- Transfer cooked quinoa to a bowl. If desired, pour over a little unsweetened almond milk for creaminess.
- Top with sliced banana, chia seeds, and a pinch of cinnamon for flavor.
- Stir to combine and enjoy warm.

Scientific Notes:

- Quinoa: This seed (often prepared and consumed like a grain) is a fantastic source of complete protein, containing all nine essential amino acids, making it exceptionally beneficial for those on an elimination diet, particularly vegetarians or those avoiding animal proteins. Its high fiber content aids digestion and can contribute to a feeling of fullness, supporting weight management.

- Chia Seeds: Known for their high omega-3 fatty acid content, chia seeds offer anti-inflammatory benefits, crucial for managing EoE symptoms. They're also high in fiber, promoting digestive health, and rich in antioxidants.

- Banana: Bananas provide a natural sweetness, reducing the need for added sugars in the diet. They are also a good source of potassium, which is essential for heart health and maintaining a healthy blood pressure level.

- Cinnamon: This spice is not only for flavor; it has anti-inflammatory properties and can help regulate blood sugar levels. It's an excellent addition to an elimination diet for its health benefits and flavor enhancement without triggering EoE symptoms.

Nutritional Information (per serving):

- Calories: ~300-350
- Protein: 8-10g

- Total Fat: 5-7g
- Fiber: 5-8g
- Sodium: Low

Avocado and Spinach Smoothie Bowl

Serves: 1

Cooking Time: 5 minutes

Ingredients and Portions/Measurements:

- Avocado: 1/2 medium (Rich in healthy fats, fiber, and EoE elimination diet-friendly)
- Baby Spinach: 1 cup (Packed with vitamins A, C, and K, iron, and EoE elimination diet-friendly)
- Unsweetened Almond Milk: 3/4 cup (For blending, ensure it's additive-free; Substitute: Hemp Milk [3/4 cup] if tolerated)
- Chia Seeds: 1 tablespoon (High in omega-3 fatty acids, fiber; Substitute: Ground Flaxseeds [1 tablespoon] if tolerated)
- Frozen Banana: 1/2 banana (Natural sweetener, high in potassium; EoE elimination diet-friendly)
- Ice Cubes: 1/2 cup (For texture, no nutritional impact)

Instructions:

- In a blender, combine the avocado, baby spinach, unsweetened almond milk, chia seeds, frozen banana, and ice cubes.
- Blend on high until smooth and creamy. If the smoothie is too thick, you can add a little more almond milk to reach your desired consistency.
- Pour the smoothie into a bowl and, if desired, top with a few additional chia seeds or slices of banana for garnish.
- Enjoy immediately for a refreshing and nutrient-packed breakfast.

Scientific Notes:

- Avocado: A great source of monounsaturated fats, avocados can help reduce inflammation in the body, which is crucial for individuals with EoE. They also provide nearly 20 vitamins, minerals, and phytonutrients, essential for overall health.
- Baby Spinach: Spinach is loaded with nutrients in a low-calorie package. Dark leafy greens like spinach are important for skin, hair, and bone health. They also provide protein, iron, vitamins, and minerals.

- Chia Seeds: Known for their high content of omega-3 fatty acids, chia seeds can help reduce inflammation and are beneficial for heart health. They're also a great source of fiber, which can aid digestion—a significant concern for those with EoE.
- Banana: Bananas act as a natural sweetener and are a good source of potassium, vitamin C, and dietary fiber. They can aid in digestion and provide energy without the need for added sugars.

Nutritional Information (per serving):

- Calories: ~300-350
- Protein: 4-6g
- Total Fat: 15-20g (mostly healthy fats)
- Fiber: 10-12g
- Sodium: Low

Sweet Potato and Kale Hash

Serves: 1

Cooking Time: 25 minutes

Ingredients and Portions/Measurements:

- Sweet Potato (medium, peeled and diced): 1/2 sweet potato (High in vitamins A and C, fiber; Phase 1 Elimination EoE diet-friendly)
- Kale (torn into pieces): 1 cup (Rich in vitamins K, A, and C, calcium; Phase 1 Elimination EoE diet-friendly)
- Olive Oil: 1 tablespoon (For cooking; Substitute: Coconut Oil [1 tablespoon] if tolerated)
- Salt (optional): To taste (Minimal use recommended; Substitute: A pinch of Himalayan pink salt if tolerated)
- Ground Turmeric: 1/4 teaspoon (Anti-inflammatory properties; Phase 1 Elimination EoE diet-friendly)
- Ground Cinnamon: 1/8 teaspoon (For flavor and blood sugar control; Phase 1 Elimination EoE diet-friendly)
- Water: 2 tablespoons (To help steam the kale, no nutritional impact)

Instructions:

- Heat olive oil in a medium skillet over medium heat. Add diced sweet potatoes. Cook for about 10 minutes, stirring occasionally, until they begin to soften.
- Sprinkle the sweet potatoes with turmeric and cinnamon, stir to coat evenly.
- Add kale and water to the skillet. Cover and let steam for 3-5 minutes until the kale has wilted and sweet potatoes are tender.
- Season with salt to taste if desired. Serve hot as a nutrient-rich breakfast hash.

Scientific Notes:

- Sweet Potato: A superb source of beta-carotene (which the body converts to vitamin A), fiber, and potassium. Sweet potatoes support eye health, promote gut health, and may enhance brain function. Their high antioxidant content helps reduce oxidative damage and inflammation, beneficial for EoE patients.
- Kale: This leafy green is loaded with nutrients and antioxidants like quercetin and kaempferol, which have powerful anti-inflammatory effects, essential for managing EoE symptoms. Kale is also an excellent

source of vitamin C, which supports the immune system, and vitamin K, crucial for bone health.

- Turmeric: Known for its curcumin content, turmeric has significant anti-inflammatory properties that can help manage EoE symptoms and overall inflammation in the body. It's also been studied for its potential to improve brain function and reduce the risk of brain diseases.
- Cinnamon: Besides adding flavor, cinnamon can lower blood sugar levels, reduce heart disease risk factors, and has a plethora of other impressive health benefits, including anti-inflammatory properties.

Nutritional Information (per serving):

- Calories: ~250-300
- Protein: 3-4g
- Total Fat: 7-10g (mostly healthy fats from olive oil)
- Fiber: 6-8g
- Sodium: Low (varies based on salt use)

Berry Chia Pudding

Serves: 1

Cooking Time: 5 minutes (plus overnight refrigeration)

Ingredients and Portions/Measurements:

- Chia Seeds: 3 tablespoons (High in omega-3 fatty acids, fiber; Phase 1 Elimination EoE diet-friendly)
- Unsweetened Almond Milk: 3/4 cup (For pudding base; Substitute: Oat Milk [3/4 cup] if tolerated)
- Mixed Berries (strawberries, blueberries, raspberries): 1/2 cup (Rich in antioxidants, vitamins; Phase 1 Elimination EoE diet-friendly)
- Pure Maple Syrup: 1 tablespoon (Natural sweetener; Substitute: Honey [1 tablespoon] if tolerated)
- Vanilla Extract: 1/2 teaspoon (For flavor enhancement; Ensure it's alcohol-free for EoE diet compliance)

Instructions:

- In a small bowl or mason jar, combine chia seeds and unsweetened almond milk. Stir well to ensure the chia seeds are fully submerged.

- Add the vanilla extract and pure maple syrup to the mixture. Stir thoroughly to combine.
- Cover the bowl or jar and refrigerate overnight, or at least for 6 hours, allowing the chia seeds to absorb the liquid and thicken into a pudding consistency.
- Before serving, stir the pudding to ensure it's evenly mixed. Top with the mixed berries.
- Enjoy a refreshing and nutritious start to your day!

Scientific Notes:

- Chia Seeds: These seeds are a nutritional powerhouse, packed with omega-3 fatty acids, which are essential for brain health and reducing inflammation in the body. The high fiber content can aid in digestion and promote a feeling of fullness, which is beneficial for weight management.
- Mixed Berries: Berries are known for their high antioxidant levels, including vitamin C and manganese, which can help protect the body from oxidative stress and reduce inflammation. They also provide a natural source of sweetness and fiber, making them an ideal ingredient for an elimination diet.

- Pure Maple Syrup: Unlike refined sugars, pure maple syrup contains vitamins and minerals like manganese and zinc. It provides a natural sweetness without the additives found in many commercial sweeteners, making it a better choice for those on an EoE diet.
- Vanilla Extract: Vanilla adds flavor complexity to the pudding. When choosing vanilla extract, ensure it's alcohol-free to comply with strict EoE diet guidelines, as alcohol can be an irritant for some individuals.

Nutritional Information (per serving):

- Calories: ~250-300
- Protein: 4-5g
- Total Fat: 8-10g (mostly healthy fats from chia seeds)
- Fiber: 10-12g
- Sodium: Low

Coconut Yogurt Parfait with Gluten-Free Granola

Serves: 1

Cooking Time: 5 minutes

Ingredients and Portions/Measurements:

- Coconut Yogurt: 3/4 cup (Dairy-free, high in probiotics; Phase 1 Elimination EoE diet-friendly)
- Gluten-Free Granola: 1/4 cup (Ensure it's free of nuts and soy; Substitute: Puffed Quinoa [1/4 cup] if granola is not tolerated)
- Fresh Blueberries: 1/4 cup (Rich in antioxidants, vitamins; Phase 1 Elimination EoE diet-friendly)
- Sliced Kiwi: 1/2 kiwi (High in vitamin C and dietary fiber; Phase 1 Elimination EoE diet-friendly)
- Honey (optional): 1 teaspoon (Natural sweetener; Substitute: Maple Syrup [1 teaspoon] if tolerated)

Instructions:

- In a serving glass or bowl, layer half of the coconut yogurt at the bottom.
- Add a layer of half the gluten-free granola over the yogurt.

- Add a layer of all the blueberries, then slice the kiwi and place it on top of the blueberries.
- Add the remaining coconut yogurt over the fruits.
- Top with the remaining gluten-free granola. Drizzle with honey or maple syrup if desired for added sweetness.
- Enjoy your nutritious and allergen-friendly breakfast parfait!

Scientific Notes:

- Coconut Yogurt: Being dairy-free, it's an excellent source of probiotics, which are beneficial for gut health. Probiotics can help maintain a healthy gut flora, crucial for individuals with EoE, as gut health is often compromised.
- Gluten-Free Granola: Provides a crunchy texture and fiber without the allergens found in traditional granolas. Fiber is essential for maintaining digestive health, which can be beneficial for individuals managing EoE.
- Blueberries and Kiwi: Both fruits are high in vitamins and antioxidants, which can help reduce inflammation in the body. Vitamin C from kiwi

supports immune function, while the antioxidants in blueberries can help protect against oxidative stress.

- Honey/Maple Syrup: Natural sweeteners are a healthier alternative to refined sugars. They can add flavor without the negative health impacts of sugar, though they should be used in moderation.

Nutritional Information (per serving):

- Calories: ~300-350
- Protein: 5-6g
- Total Fat: 8-10g (mostly healthy fats from coconut yogurt)
- Fiber: 4-5g
- Sodium: Low

LUNCH RECIPES

EMPIRIC ELIMINATION DIET

Grilled Chicken Salad with Avocado
Dressing

Serves: 1

Cooking Time: 20 minutes

Ingredients and Portions/Measurements:

- Chicken Breast (skinless, boneless): 1 small (High in protein; Substitute: Grilled Tofu [100g] if poultry is not tolerated)
- Mixed Salad Greens: 2 cups (Rich in vitamins, minerals; Phase 1 Elimination EoE diet-friendly)
- Cucumber (sliced): 1/2 medium (Hydrating, contains antioxidants; Phase 1 Elimination EoE diet-friendly)
- Carrots (shredded): 1/4 cup (High in beta-carotene, fiber; Phase 1 Elimination EoE diet-friendly)
- Avocado: 1/4 medium (For dressing, rich in healthy fats; Phase 1 Elimination EoE diet-friendly)
- Olive Oil: 1 teaspoon (For grilling chicken; Substitute: Coconut Oil [1 teaspoon] if preferred)

- Lemon Juice: 1 tablespoon (For dressing, vitamin C source; Phase 1 Elimination EoE diet-friendly)
- Salt and Pepper: To taste (Minimize salt for a lower sodium option; Phase 1 Elimination EoE diet-friendly)

Instructions:

- Preheat the grill to medium-high heat. Brush the chicken breast with olive oil and season with salt and pepper.
- Grill the chicken for about 6-7 minutes on each side, or until fully cooked and no longer pink inside. Let it rest for a few minutes, then slice thinly.
- For the avocado dressing, blend the avocado, lemon juice, and a pinch of salt and pepper until smooth. Add a little water if needed to reach your desired consistency.
- In a large bowl, toss the mixed greens, sliced cucumber, and shredded carrots.
- Top the salad with the sliced grilled chicken (or tofu) and drizzle with the avocado dressing.
- Serve immediately for a refreshing and nutritious lunch.

Scientific Notes:

- Chicken Breast: A lean source of high-quality protein, chicken helps in muscle repair and growth. It's also a good source of vitamins B6 and B12, which are important for energy metabolism and brain health.
- Mixed Salad Greens: Dark leafy greens are loaded with vitamins A, C, K, and minerals like iron and calcium. They're low in calories, support heart health, and have anti-inflammatory properties.
- Avocado: Rich in monounsaturated fats, avocados can help reduce inflammation and are linked to heart health benefits. They're also high in fiber, potassium, and vitamins C, E, and K.
- Lemon Juice: Provides vitamin C, which supports immune function and skin health. It also acts as an antioxidant, helping to protect cells from damage.

Nutritional Information (per serving):

- Calories: ~400-450
- Protein: 25-30g
- Total Fat: 20-25g (mostly healthy fats from avocado and olive oil)
- Fiber: 6-8g
- Sodium: Low (varies based on salt usage)

Turmeric Quinoa Vegetable Bowl

Serves: 1

Cooking Time: 25 minutes

Ingredients and Portions/Measurements:

- Quinoa: 1/2 cup (A complete protein, gluten-free; Phase 1 Elimination EoE diet-friendly)

- Water: 1 cup (For cooking quinoa, no nutritional impact)

- Olive Oil: 1 teaspoon (For sautéing vegetables; Substitute: Avocado Oil [1 teaspoon] if preferred)

- Turmeric: 1/2 teaspoon (Anti-inflammatory properties; Phase 1 Elimination EoE diet-friendly)

- Cumin: 1/4 teaspoon (For flavor, aids digestion; Phase 1 Elimination EoE diet-friendly)

- Salt: A pinch (To taste, minimize for a lower sodium option; Phase 1 Elimination EoE diet-friendly)

- Carrot (diced): 1/2 medium (High in beta-carotene, fiber; Phase 1 Elimination EoE diet-friendly)

- Zucchini (diced): 1/2 medium (Good source of vitamins A, C, and fiber; Phase 1 Elimination EoE diet-friendly)

- Red Bell Pepper (diced): 1/4 medium (Rich in vitamin C and antioxidants; Phase 1 Elimination EoE diet-friendly)
- Fresh Spinach: 1 cup (Packed with vitamins K, A, C; Phase 1 Elimination EoE diet-friendly)

Instructions:

- Rinse the quinoa under cold water until the water runs clear. In a saucepan, bring 1 cup of water to a boil. Add quinoa, cover, and simmer on low heat for 15 minutes or until all water is absorbed. Let it sit covered for 5 minutes, then fluff with a fork.
- While the quinoa cooks, heat olive oil in a skillet over medium heat. Add the diced carrot, zucchini, and bell pepper. Sauté for 5-7 minutes until just tender.
- Stir in turmeric, cumin, and a pinch of salt to the vegetables, mixing well to evenly coat.
- Add the spinach to the skillet, stirring until wilted, about 2 minutes.
- Serve the sautéed vegetables over the cooked quinoa in a bowl. Mix gently to combine.

Scientific Notes:

- Quinoa: Known for its high protein content, including all nine essential amino acids, quinoa is an excellent choice for those on elimination diets. It's also a good source of fiber and minerals, supporting digestive health and satiety.
- Turmeric: Contains curcumin, a compound with strong anti-inflammatory and antioxidant properties. Turmeric can help reduce inflammation in the body, beneficial for managing EoE symptoms.
- Cumin: Besides adding a warm flavor, cumin has been shown to aid digestion and improve immune function with its antibacterial properties.
- Vegetables: The combination of carrot, zucchini, and red bell pepper provides a variety of vitamins, minerals, and antioxidants. These nutrients support immune function, eye health, and can help reduce inflammation.

Nutritional Information (per serving):

- Calories: ~300-350
- Protein: 8-10g
- Total Fat: 5-7g (mostly healthy fats from olive oil)
- Fiber: 6-8g

- Sodium: Low (varies based on salt usage)

Lemon-Herb Baked Cod with Zucchini Noodles

Serves: 1

Cooking Time: 20 minutes

Ingredients and Portions/Measurements:

- Cod Fillet: 1 medium (Rich in omega-3 fatty acids, protein; Phase 1 Elimination EoE diet-friendly)
- Lemon Juice: 2 tablespoons (Vitamin C source, enhances flavor; Phase 1 Elimination EoE diet-friendly)
- Fresh Dill: 1 tablespoon, chopped (For flavor, supports digestion; Phase 1 Elimination EoE diet-friendly)
- Olive Oil: 1 teaspoon (For baking, healthy fats; Substitute: Avocado Oil [1 teaspoon] if preferred)
- Zucchini: 1 large (Turned into noodles, high in fiber, vitamins; Phase 1 Elimination EoE diet-friendly)
- Salt and Pepper: To taste (Minimize salt for a lower sodium option; Phase 1 Elimination EoE diet-friendly)

Instructions:

- Preheat your oven to 375°F (190°C). Place the cod fillet on a piece of aluminum foil or a baking dish.
- Drizzle lemon juice over the cod. Sprinkle with chopped dill, and season with salt and pepper. Drizzle with olive oil.
- Wrap the cod in aluminum foil or cover the baking dish. Bake in the preheated oven for about 12-15 minutes, or until the fish flakes easily with a fork.
- While the cod is baking, use a spiralizer or a vegetable peeler to create zucchini noodles (zoodles).
- Heat a non-stick pan over medium heat. Add the zucchini noodles and sauté for 3-5 minutes until tender. Season with a pinch of salt and pepper.
- Serve the baked cod over the bed of zucchini noodles. Garnish with additional lemon wednesday or fresh dill if desired.

Scientific Notes:

- Cod: A lean protein source that is high in omega-3 fatty acids, which are essential for reducing inflammation in the body and supporting brain health. Suitable for those on an elimination diet, especially when avoiding common allergens.

- Lemon Juice: Provides vitamin C, which is crucial for immune system support and acts as an antioxidant, reducing oxidative stress and inflammation.
- Fresh Dill: Besides adding a fresh flavor, dill has properties that may aid in digestion and provide minor anti-inflammatory benefits.
- Zucchini: Low in calories but high in fiber, vitamins A and C, and potassium. Zucchini noodles offer a nutritious, gluten-free alternative to traditional pasta, supporting gut health and providing essential nutrients.

Nutritional Information (per serving):

- Calories: ~250-300
- Protein: 22-25g
- Total Fat: 8-10g (mostly healthy fats from olive oil and fish)
- Fiber: 2-3g
- Sodium: Low (varies based on salt usage)

Butternut Squash Soup with Ginger

Serves: 1

Cooking Time: 30 minutes

Ingredients and Portions/Measurements:

- Butternut Squash: 2 cups, peeled and cubed (Rich in vitamins A and C, fiber; Phase 1 Elimination EoE diet-friendly)
- Olive Oil: 1 teaspoon (For roasting, healthy fats; Substitute: Coconut Oil [1 teaspoon] if preferred)
- Fresh Ginger: 1 tablespoon, minced (Aids digestion, anti-inflammatory; Phase 1 Elimination EoE diet-friendly)
- Vegetable Broth: 2 cups (Ensure it's allergen-free; Substitute: Homemade Broth [2 cups] if necessary)
- Salt: A pinch (To taste, minimize for a lower sodium option; Phase 1 Elimination EoE diet-friendly)
- Ground Cinnamon: 1/4 teaspoon (Anti-inflammatory properties; Phase 1 Elimination EoE diet-friendly)
- Ground Nutmeg: A pinch (For flavor; Phase 1 Elimination EoE diet-friendly)
- Water (optional): To adjust consistency

Instructions:

- Preheat the oven to 400°F (200°C). Toss the cubed butternut squash with olive oil and a pinch of salt, then spread on a baking sheet. Roast for about 20 minutes or until tender and slightly caramelized.
- In a large pot over medium heat, add the roasted butternut squash, minced ginger, vegetable broth, cinnamon, and nutmeg. Bring to a simmer.
- Cook for about 10 minutes to allow the flavors to meld together. Remove from heat and let it cool slightly.
- Using an immersion blender or a regular blender, puree the soup until smooth. If the soup is too thick, you can add a little water to reach your desired consistency.
- Taste and adjust the seasoning with salt if needed.
- Serve warm, garnished with a swirl of olive oil or a sprinkle of cinnamon.

Scientific Notes:

- Butternut Squash: High in beta-carotene, which the body converts to vitamin A, essential for immune function and eye health. It's also a good source of vitamin C and dietary fiber, supporting digestive health.

- Ginger: Contains gingerol, a substance with powerful anti-inflammatory and antioxidant effects. Ginger can help reduce nausea and improve digestion, making it beneficial for individuals with EoE.
- Cinnamon and Nutmeg: Both spices add not only flavor but also contain anti-inflammatory properties. Cinnamon has been linked to lower blood sugar levels and improved heart health.

Nutritional Information (per serving):

- Calories: ~200-250
- Protein: 2-3g
- Total Fat: 5-7g (mostly healthy fats from olive oil)
- Fiber: 5-6g
- Sodium: Low (varies based on broth and added salt)

Mediterranean Chickpea Salad

Serves: 1

Cooking Time: 10 minutes

Ingredients and Portions/Measurements:

- Chickpeas (cooked, rinsed): 1 cup (Rich in protein, fiber; Phase 1 Elimination EoE diet-friendly)
- Cucumber (diced): 1/2 medium (Hydration, vitamins; Phase 1 Elimination EoE diet-friendly)
- Cherry Tomatoes (halved): 1/2 cup (Vitamin C, antioxidants; Phase 1 Elimination EoE diet-friendly)
- Red Onion (finely chopped): 2 tablespoons (Flavor, anti-inflammatory properties; Phase 1 Elimination EoE diet-friendly)
- Fresh Parsley (chopped): 1/4 cup (Vitamins A, C, and K; Phase 1 Elimination EoE diet-friendly)
- Lemon Juice: 1 tablespoon (For dressing, vitamin C source; Phase 1 Elimination EoE diet-friendly)
- Olive Oil: 1 teaspoon (Healthy fats; Substitute: Avocado Oil [1 teaspoon] if preferred)
- Salt and Pepper: To taste (Minimize salt for lower sodium; Phase 1 Elimination EoE diet-friendly)

Instructions:

- In a large mixing bowl, combine the chickpeas, diced cucumber, halved cherry tomatoes, finely chopped red onion, and chopped parsley.
- In a small bowl, whisk together the lemon juice, olive oil, and a pinch of salt and pepper to create the dressing.
- Pour the dressing over the salad and toss to coat evenly.
- Taste and adjust the seasoning if necessary. Let the salad sit for a few minutes to marinate for enhanced flavor.
- Serve the salad chilled or at room temperature for a refreshing and nutritious lunch.

Scientific Notes:

- Chickpeas: A great source of plant-based protein and dietary fiber, which can aid in digestion and promote satiety. Chickpeas are also rich in vitamins and minerals, including iron and phosphorus, supporting overall health.
- Cucumber and Cherry Tomatoes: Provide hydration and are high in various vitamins and antioxidants.

These vegetables can support heart health and provide anti-inflammatory benefits.

- Lemon Juice and Olive Oil: The combination not only adds flavor but also provides vitamin C from the lemon and healthy monounsaturated fats from the olive oil, which are beneficial for heart health and can help with the absorption of vitamins.

Nutritional Information (per serving):

- Calories: ~250-300
- Protein: 9-11g
- Total Fat: 5-7g (mostly healthy fats)
- Fiber: 6-8g
- Sodium: Low (varies based on salt usage)

DINNER RECIPES

EMPIRIC ELIMINATION DIET

Roasted Salmon with Steamed Broccoli and Quinoa

Serves: 1

Cooking Time: 30 minutes

Ingredients and Portions/Measurements:

- Salmon Fillet: 1 (4-ounce) piece (Rich in omega-3 fatty acids, protein; Phase 1 Elimination EoE diet-friendly)
- Quinoa: 1/2 cup (A complete protein, gluten-free; Phase 1 Elimination EoE diet-friendly)
- Broccoli Florets: 1 cup (High in vitamins C and K, fiber; Phase 1 Elimination EoE diet-friendly)
- Olive Oil: 1 teaspoon (For roasting salmon; Substitute: Avocado Oil [1 teaspoon] if preferred)
- Lemon Wedges: 2 (For flavor, vitamin C source; Phase 1 Elimination EoE diet-friendly)
- Salt and Pepper: To taste (Minimize salt for a lower sodium option; Phase 1 Elimination EoE diet-friendly)

Instructions:

- Preheat the oven to 400°F (200°C). Place the salmon fillet on a baking sheet lined with parchment paper. Drizzle with olive oil and season with salt and pepper. Place lemon wedges around the salmon.
- Roast in the preheated oven for about 12-15 minutes, or until the salmon is cooked through and flakes easily with a fork.
- While the salmon is roasting, rinse the quinoa under cold water. Bring 1 cup of water to a boil in a small pot. Add quinoa, reduce heat to low, cover, and simmer for 15 minutes or until all the water is absorbed. Let it sit covered for 5 minutes, then fluff with a fork.
- Steam the broccoli florets until tender but still bright green, about 3-5 minutes.
- Serve the roasted salmon with a side of fluffy quinoa and steamed broccoli. Squeeze the roasted lemon wedges over the salmon for extra flavor.

Scientific Notes:

- Salmon: A great source of omega-3 fatty acids, which are essential for reducing inflammation in the body and supporting heart and brain health. Salmon is also a high-quality source of protein.

- Quinoa: Contains all nine essential amino acids, making it a complete protein source. It's also high in fiber and minerals, such as magnesium and iron, supporting overall health and digestion.
- Broccoli: Rich in vitamins C and K, as well as fiber, antioxidants, and bioactive compounds that may protect against cancer. Broccoli's nutrients support immune function and gut health.
- Lemon: Provides vitamin C, which is crucial for the immune system. The acidity of lemon can enhance the absorption of iron from plant-based foods like quinoa.

Nutritional Information (per serving):

- Calories: ~400-450
- Protein: 25-30g
- Total Fat: 15-20g (mostly healthy fats from salmon and olive oil)
- Fiber: 5-7g
- Sodium: Low (varies based on salt usage)

Eggplant and Tomato Bake with Basil Pesto

Serves: 1

Cooking Time: 45 minutes

Ingredients and Portions/Measurements:

- Eggplant: 1 medium, sliced into rounds (High in fiber, antioxidants; Phase 1 Elimination EoE diet-friendly)
- Tomato: 2 medium, sliced (Rich in vitamin C, lycopene; Phase 1 Elimination EoE diet-friendly)
- Olive Oil: 1 tablespoon (For baking, contains healthy fats; Substitute: Avocado Oil [1 tablespoon] if preferred)
- Fresh Basil Leaves: 1/4 cup (For pesto, anti-inflammatory; Phase 1 Elimination EoE diet-friendly)
- Garlic: 1 clove, minced (For pesto, anti-inflammatory; Substitute: Asafoetida Powder [a pinch] for a low FODMAP option)
- Pine Nuts: 1 tablespoon (For pesto, rich in vitamins, minerals; Substitute: Sunflower Seeds [1 tablespoon] if nuts are not tolerated)
- Lemon Juice: 1 teaspoon (For pesto, vitamin C source; Phase 1 Elimination EoE diet-friendly)

- Salt and Pepper: To taste (Minimize salt for a lower sodium option; Phase 1 Elimination EoE diet-friendly)

Instructions:

- Preheat your oven to 375°F (190°C). Brush both sides of the eggplant slices with olive oil and season with salt and pepper. Arrange them in a single layer on a baking sheet.
- Bake the eggplant for 25-30 minutes, flipping halfway through, until tender and golden.
- While the eggplant is baking, prepare the basil pesto. In a food processor, blend the basil leaves, garlic (or asafoetida powder), pine nuts (or sunflower seeds), lemon juice, and a drizzle of olive oil until smooth. Season with salt and pepper to taste.
- In a baking dish, layer the roasted eggplant slices with tomato slices. Spoon the basil pesto over the top of each layer.
- Return the dish to the oven and bake for an additional 10-15 minutes, until the tomatoes are just softened.
- Serve hot, garnished with additional fresh basil leaves if desired.

Scientific Notes:

- Eggplant: Contains nasunin, a potent antioxidant that helps protect cell membranes from damage. Eggplant is also a good source of fiber, which supports digestive health.
- Tomato: High in lycopene, an antioxidant linked to reduced risk of heart disease and cancer. Tomatoes are also a great source of vitamin C, potassium, folate, and vitamin K.
- Basil Pesto: Basil is known for its anti-inflammatory properties and high levels of antioxidants. Pine nuts (or sunflower seeds) add essential fats, protein, and additional antioxidants.
- Lemon Juice: Enhances the absorption of non-heme iron from plant sources and adds a refreshing flavor while contributing vitamin C.

Nutritional Information (per serving):

- Calories: ~300-350
- Protein: 5-6g
- Total Fat: 15-20g (mostly healthy fats from olive oil and pine nuts/sunflower seeds)
- Fiber: 8-10g
- Sodium: Low (varies based on salt usage)

Stir-Fried Tofu with Mixed Vegetables and Brown Rice

Serves: 1

Cooking Time: 30 minutes

Ingredients and Portions/Measurements:

- Tofu (firm, pressed and cubed): 1/2 cup (Rich in protein, iron; Phase 1 Elimination EoE diet-friendly)
- Brown Rice: 1/2 cup (cooked) (High in fiber, B vitamins; Phase 1 Elimination EoE diet-friendly)
- Carrots (thinly sliced): 1/4 cup (Beta-carotene, fiber; Phase 1 Elimination EoE diet-friendly)
- Bell Pepper (any color, sliced): 1/4 cup (Vitamin C, antioxidants; Phase 1 Elimination EoE diet-friendly)
- Zucchini (sliced): 1/4 cup (Vitamins A and C, potassium; Phase 1 Elimination EoE diet-friendly)
- Olive Oil: 1 teaspoon (For stir-frying; Substitute: Avocado Oil [1 teaspoon] if preferred)
- Garlic (minced): 1 clove (Flavor, anti-inflammatory; Substitute: Garlic-Infused Oil for a low FODMAP option)
- Ginger (minced): 1 teaspoon (Digestive aid, anti-inflammatory; Phase 1 Elimination EoE diet-friendly)

- Soy Sauce (gluten-free, low sodium): 1 tablespoon (Flavor; Substitute: Coconut Aminos [1 tablespoon] if soy is not tolerated)
- Salt and Pepper: To taste (Minimize salt for a lower sodium option; Phase 1 Elimination EoE diet-friendly)

Instructions:

- Start by cooking the brown rice according to package instructions. Set aside and keep warm.
- Heat olive oil in a large skillet or wok over medium-high heat. Add the minced garlic and ginger, sautéing for about 1 minute until fragrant.
- Increase the heat to high and add the cubed tofu to the skillet. Stir-fry for 3-5 minutes until golden brown on all sides.
- Add the sliced carrots, bell pepper, and zucchini to the skillet. Stir-fry for an additional 5-7 minutes until the vegetables are tender but still crisp.
- Pour the soy sauce (or coconut aminos) over the tofu and vegetables, stirring to coat evenly. Season with salt and pepper to taste.
- Serve the stir-fried tofu and vegetables over the warm brown rice.

Scientific Notes:

- Tofu: A great source of plant-based protein and contains all nine essential amino acids. It's also a good source of iron and calcium, which are important for bone health and oxygen transport in the body.
- Brown Rice: Rich in magnesium, which is vital for heart health and bone strength. The high fiber content aids in digestion and helps maintain stable blood sugar levels.
- Vegetables: A mix of carrots, bell peppers, and zucchini provides a broad range of vitamins, minerals, and antioxidants, which can help reduce inflammation and support immune function.
- Ginger and Garlic: Both have significant anti-inflammatory properties and can aid digestion. Ginger is particularly known for its ability to alleviate gastrointestinal irritation.

Nutritional Information (per serving):

- Calories: ~400-450
- Protein: 15-20g
- Total Fat: 10-12g (mostly healthy fats from olive oil)
- Fiber: 5-7g

- Sodium: Low to moderate (varies based on soy sauce and added salt)

Herb-Roasted Turkey Breast with Sweet Potato Mash

Serves: 1

Cooking Time: 1 hour

Ingredients and Portions/Measurements:

- Turkey Breast (skinless, boneless): 6 ounces (High in protein, selenium; Phase 1 Elimination EoE diet-friendly)
- Olive Oil: 1 teaspoon (For roasting turkey; Substitute: Avocado Oil [1 teaspoon] if preferred)
- Fresh Rosemary: 1 tablespoon, chopped (Anti-inflammatory, aids digestion; Phase 1 Elimination EoE diet-friendly)
- Fresh Thyme: 1 tablespoon, chopped (Antioxidant properties; Phase 1 Elimination EoE diet-friendly)
- Sweet Potato: 1 medium (Rich in beta-carotene, vitamins; Phase 1 Elimination EoE diet-friendly)
- Salt and Pepper: To taste (Minimize salt for a lower sodium option; Phase 1 Elimination EoE diet-friendly)

Instructions:

- Preheat your oven to 375°F (190°C). Rub the turkey breast with olive oil and season with chopped rosemary, thyme, salt, and pepper.
- Place the turkey breast on a baking sheet and roast in the preheated oven for about 45 minutes, or until the internal temperature reaches 165°F (74°C). Let it rest for 10 minutes before slicing.
- While the turkey is roasting, pierce the sweet potato several times with a fork and place it in the oven alongside the turkey. Bake until tender, about 45 minutes.
- Once the sweet potato is cooked, let it cool slightly before peeling and mashing it in a bowl. Season with a pinch of salt and pepper to taste.
- Serve the sliced herb-roasted turkey breast alongside the sweet potato mash.

Scientific Notes:

- Turkey Breast: A lean source of high-quality protein that is low in fat. Turkey is also a good source of selenium, which plays a key role in thyroid hormone metabolism and antioxidant defense systems.

- Sweet Potato: High in beta-carotene, which the body converts into vitamin A, essential for immune function, vision, and skin health. Sweet potatoes are also a good source of dietary fiber, promoting digestive health.
- Rosemary and Thyme: Both herbs not only add flavor without the need for salt but also contain compounds with antioxidant and anti-inflammatory properties, potentially benefiting those with EoE by reducing inflammation.

Nutritional Information (per serving):

- Calories: ~400-450
- Protein: 35-40g
- Total Fat: 10-15g (mostly healthy fats from olive oil)
- Fiber: 5-6g
- Sodium: Low (varies based on salt usage)

Grilled Lemon-Garlic Shrimp with Asparagus

Serves: 1

Cooking Time: 20 minutes

Ingredients and Portions/Measurements:

- Shrimp (peeled and deveined): 6 ounces (Rich in protein, selenium; Phase 1 Elimination EoE diet-friendly)
- Asparagus: 1 cup (trimmed and cut into pieces, high in vitamins A, C, E, and K; Phase 1 Elimination EoE diet-friendly)
- Olive Oil: 1 teaspoon (For grilling, healthy fats; Substitute: Avocado Oil [1 teaspoon] if preferred)
- Garlic: 1 clove, minced (Flavor, anti-inflammatory; Substitute: Asafoetida Powder [a pinch] for a low FODMAP option)
- Lemon Juice: 1 tablespoon (For marinade, vitamin C source; Phase 1 Elimination EoE diet-friendly)
- Lemon Zest: 1 teaspoon (For flavor; Phase 1 Elimination EoE diet-friendly)
- Salt and Pepper: To taste (Minimize salt for a lower sodium option; Phase 1 Elimination EoE diet-friendly)

Instructions:

- In a bowl, combine the shrimp with olive oil, minced garlic (or asafoetida powder), lemon juice, lemon zest, salt, and pepper. Let marinate for 10-15 minutes.
- Preheat your grill or grill pan over medium-high heat. Thread the shrimp onto skewers (if using a grill) and place the asparagus on a piece of aluminum foil or a grill basket.
- Grill the shrimp for 2-3 minutes on each side or until they turn pink and are cooked through. Simultaneously, grill the asparagus, turning occasionally, until tender and charred, about 5-7 minutes.
- Serve the grilled shrimp and asparagus together, garnished with additional lemon wedges if desired.

Scientific Notes:

- Shrimp: A lean source of high-quality protein that's low in calories and rich in several minerals, including selenium and phosphorus. Selenium is important for thyroid function and the immune system.
- Asparagus: Contains a variety of antioxidants such as vitamins A, C, and E, which can help combat oxidative

stress. It's also rich in vitamin K, essential for blood clotting and bone health.

- Lemon Juice and Zest: Lemon is not only a good source of vitamin C, which is vital for the immune system and skin health, but also adds a refreshing flavor. The zest provides beneficial plant compounds.

Nutritional Information (per serving):

- Calories: ~250-300
- Protein: 25-30g
- Total Fat: 10-12g (mostly healthy fats from olive oil)
- Fiber: 3-4g
- Sodium: Low (varies based on salt usage)

7 DAYS MEAL PLAN FOR EMPRIC ELIMINATION STAGE

Day 1:

Breakfast*:* Quinoa Breakfast Bowl

Lunch: Grilled Chicken Salad with Avocado Dressing

Dinner: Roasted Salmon with Steamed Broccoli and Quinoa

Day 2:

Breakfast: Avocado and Spinach Smoothie Bowl

Lunch: Turmeric Quinoa Vegetable Bowl

Dinner: Eggplant and Tomato Bake with Basil Pesto

Day 3:

Breakfast: Sweet Potato and Kale Hash

Lunch: Lemon-Herb Baked Cod with Zucchini Noodles

Dinner: Stir-Fried Tofu with Mixed Vegetables and Brown Rice

Day 4:

Breakfast: Berry Chia Pudding

Lunch: Butternut Squash Soup with Ginger

Dinner: Herb-Roasted Turkey Breast with Sweet Potato Mash

Day 5:

Breakfast: Coconut Yogurt Parfait with Gluten-Free Granola

Lunch: Mediterranean Chickpea Salad

Dinner: Grilled Lemon-Garlic Shrimp with Asparagus

Day 6:

Breakfast: Quinoa Breakfast Bowl

Lunch: Turmeric Quinoa Vegetable Bowl

Dinner: Eggplant and Tomato Bake with Basil Pesto

Day 7:

Breakfast: Sweet Potato and Kale Hash

Lunch: Grilled Chicken Salad with Avocado Dressing

Dinner: Stir-Fried Tofu with Mixed Vegetables and Brown Rice

MEAL PLANNER

NEGLECT THE SNACKS AND APPETIZER

AMOS JIMMY
DAILY MEAL PLANNER

DATE ———————————————   M T W T F S S
:

BREAKFAST   ### DINNER

LUNCH

NOTES

SNACKS

JIMMY'S CULINARY HAVEN

Moving Forward To Phase 2: Welcome To A World Of New Flavors

As we leave behind the initial stage of the Empiric Elimination Diet, where we focused on avoiding six key ingredients to manage eosinophilic esophagitis (EoE), it's time to step into the next chapter of your dietary journey. We warmly welcome you to Phase 2, an exciting period of reintroducing foods back into your diet.

In this phase, our goal is to gradually and safely reintroduce foods, allowing us to identify any potential triggers for EoE while ensuring a balanced and nutritious diet. We understand the importance of making this transition smooth and enjoyable for beginners, offering a range of meal options that are not only healthful but also delicious and easy to prepare.

As we embark on this journey together, we encourage you to explore a variety of breakfast, lunch, and dinner recipes tailored to meet your dietary needs. These recipes have been carefully curated to ensure they are suitable for those moving on from the strict elimination of certain foods, focusing on introducing a diverse array of ingredients to your meals in a controlled manner.

We believe that your feedback and experiences are invaluable as we continue to refine and enhance our meal plans. Your insights will help us to ensure that our recommendations support your dietary needs effectively, allowing for a smoother transition through the phases of the diet.

Thank you for your commitment to your health and dietary management through this approach. Your dedication is a key component of our community's ongoing success. As we proceed to introduce more varied and health-conscious meal options, we look forward to your active participation and continued feedback. Together, we can navigate the complexities of the diet with confidence and success, paving the way for a healthier, more enjoyable dietary experience.

CHAPTER 3

BREAKFAST RECIPES
REINTRODUCTION STAGE PHASE 2

Fluffy Almond Milk and Chia Pancakes

Serves: 1

Cooking Time: 15 minutes

Ingredients and Portions/Measurements:

- Almond Milk: 3/4 cup (A dairy-free alternative, high in vitamin E and calcium, suitable for EoE diet phase 2 reintroduction)
- Substitution (if milk triggers): Coconut milk 3/4 cup (Also dairy-free, rich in vitamins C, E, B1, B3, B5, and B6)
- Gluten-Free Flour: 1 cup (Suitable for gluten sensitivities, provides a base without triggering gluten-related EoE symptoms)
- Egg: 1 large (A common reintroduction in phase 2; rich in protein and B vitamins)
- Substitution (if egg triggers): Flaxseed meal mixed with water (1 tbsp flaxseed meal + 2.5 tbsp water, left

to sit for 5 minutes; mimics the binding properties of eggs and adds omega-3 fatty acids)

- Chia Seeds: 2 tbsp (Rich in omega-3 fatty acids, fiber, and antioxidants, suitable for EoE-friendly diets)
- Baking Powder: 1 tsp (Ensures fluffiness, without significant nutritional impact)
- Salt: A pinch (For flavor enhancement, use minimally to manage sodium intake)
- Olive Oil or Coconut Oil: For cooking (Heart-healthy fats, use sparingly)

Instructions:

- Mix Dry Ingredients: In a bowl, combine gluten-free flour, baking powder, chia seeds, and a pinch of salt.
- Add Wet Ingredients: Make a well in the center of the dry ingredients. Add the egg (or flaxseed mixture) and almond milk (or coconut milk). Mix until you achieve a smooth batter.
- Let Sit: Allow the batter to sit for 5 minutes. Chia seeds will slightly thicken the mixture.
- Cook Pancakes: Heat a non-stick pan over medium heat and brush with a small amount of oil. Pour 1/4 cup of batter for each pancake. Cook until bubbles

form on the surface, then flip and cook until golden brown.

- Serve: Enjoy hot with a drizzle of maple syrup or fresh fruits if tolerated.

Scientific Notes:

- Almond Milk and Coconut Milk: Both are excellent dairy substitutes. Almond milk is low in calories and rich in vitamin E, an antioxidant. Coconut milk is higher in calories but provides a good dose of medium-chain triglycerides (MCTs), beneficial for energy. Both options are suitable for those with eosinophilic esophagitis (EoE) during the reintroduction phase, offering nutrients without the risk of dairy-triggered symptoms.
- Flaxseed Meal: A wonderful egg substitute that provides alpha-linolenic acid (ALA), a type of omega-3 fatty acid important for heart health and anti-inflammatory properties. The fiber in flaxseed can also help with digestion, making it a beneficial addition for individuals managing EoE.

Nutritional Information (per serving, with almond milk and egg):

- Calories: Approximately 350-400

- Protein: 10-15g
- Total Fat: 10-15g (depending on oil used for cooking)
- Fiber: 5-7g
- Sodium: Low

Avocado and Quinoa Breakfast Bowl

Serves: 1

Cooking Time: 20 minutes

Ingredients and Portions/Measurements:

- Quinoa: 1/2 cup (A complete protein source, rich in fiber, vitamins, and minerals, phase 2 reintroduction EoE diet friendly)
- Water: 1 cup (For cooking quinoa, no nutritional impact)
- Avocado: 1/2 (Rich in healthy fats, fiber, and potassium, suitable for most EoE diets)
- Cooked Spinach: 1/4 cup (High in iron and calcium, can be reintroduced in phase 2 for its nutritional benefits)
- Pumpkin Seeds: 1 tablespoon (A good source of zinc, magnesium, and healthy fats)

- Substitution (if seeds trigger): Ground flaxseed 1 tablespoon (Provides omega-3 fatty acids and fiber, less likely to trigger symptoms in some patients)
- Almond Milk (for dressing): 2 tablespoons (If reintroduced successfully; rich in vitamin E)
- Substitution (if almond milk triggers): Coconut yogurt 2 tablespoons (Dairy-free, adds creaminess and probiotics for gut health)
- Lemon Juice: 1 teaspoon (For dressing, adds vitamin C and enhances iron absorption from spinach)
- Salt and Pepper: To taste (Use minimally to manage sodium intake)

Instructions:

- Cook Quinoa: Rinse quinoa under cold water. In a pot, bring 1 cup of water to a boil. Add quinoa, reduce heat to low, cover, and simmer for 15 minutes or until water is absorbed. Remove from heat and let sit covered for 5 minutes. Fluff with a fork.
- Prepare Dressing: In a small bowl, whisk together almond milk (or coconut yogurt) and lemon juice. Season with a pinch of salt and pepper.
- Assemble Bowl: In a serving bowl, place cooked quinoa at the bottom. Top with sliced avocado, cooked

spinach, and pumpkin seeds (or ground flaxseed). Drizzle with the prepared dressing.

- Serve: Enjoy immediately, mixing all the ingredients well before eating.

Scientific Notes:

- Quinoa: This grain is a valuable part of the diet for individuals with EoE. It's not only gluten-free but also a complete protein, providing all nine essential amino acids. Quinoa's high fiber content supports digestive health, an important aspect for EoE management.
- Avocado: Offers a rich source of monounsaturated fats, particularly beneficial for heart health. Its fiber content is also key for maintaining a healthy digestive system.
- Pumpkin Seeds and Ground Flaxseed: Both are excellent sources of minerals and omega-3 fatty acids, respectively. They contribute to a healthy diet by providing essential nutrients. While seeds can be a trigger for some, ground flaxseed is often a safer alternative, offering similar nutritional benefits without the risk of aggravating EoE symptoms.
- Coconut Yogurt: A great alternative for those sensitive to almond milk, it introduces probiotics into the diet,

which can aid in maintaining a healthy gut microbiota.

Nutritional Information (per serving, with almond milk and pumpkin seeds):

- Calories: Approximately 300-350
- Protein: 8-12g
- Total Fat: 15-20g
- Fiber: 6-8g
- Sodium: Low

Berry Smoothie Bowl with Egg-Free Protein

Serves: 1

Cooking Time: 10 minutes

Ingredients and Portions/Measurements:

- Mixed Berries (blueberries, strawberries, raspberries): 1 cup (Rich in antioxidants, vitamins, and fiber, suitable for EoE diet)
- Spinach: 1/2 cup (High in iron and vitamin K, phase 2 reintroduction EoE diet friendly)
- Chia Seeds: 1 tablespoon (Rich in omega-3 fatty acids and fiber, a good substitution for traditional protein sources)
- Almond Milk: 3/4 cup (A dairy-free alternative, high in vitamin E and calcium, suitable for EoE diet phase 2 reintroduction)
- Substitution (if almond milk triggers): Oat milk 3/4 cup (Also dairy-free, rich in vitamins B and fiber)
- Protein Powder (egg-free, dairy-free): 1 scoop (To add protein without eggs or dairy, choose a plant-based option like pea or hemp protein)
- Banana: 1/2 (For natural sweetness and creaminess, plus potassium)

- Optional Toppings:
- Granola (gluten-free): 2 tablespoons (If tolerated; provides texture and additional nutrients)
- Coconut Flakes: 1 tablespoon (For healthy fats and flavor)

Instructions:

- Blend Smoothie Base: In a blender, combine mixed berries, spinach, chia seeds, almond milk (or oat milk), protein powder, and banana. Blend until smooth.
- Adjust Consistency: If the smoothie is too thick, add a little more almond/oat milk to reach your desired consistency.
- Serve: Pour the smoothie into a bowl. If using, sprinkle the top with gluten-free granola and coconut flakes.
- Enjoy: Eat immediately with a spoon, enjoying the mix of flavors and textures.

Scientific Notes:

- Mixed Berries: Berries are an excellent source of antioxidants, such as vitamin C and manganese, which can help protect the body from oxidative stress and inflammation, potentially beneficial for EoE management.

- Chia Seeds: These seeds are not only a good source of omega-3 fatty acids but also provide considerable amounts of fiber, which can help with digestion. Their gel-forming property when mixed with liquids can aid in creating a satisfying texture and contribute to hydration.

- Almond and Oat Milk: Both are excellent dairy substitutes. Almond milk is lower in calories and rich in vitamin E, while oat milk is a good source of vitamin B and fiber. They provide options for those with EoE to enjoy creamy textures without dairy.

- Plant-based Protein Powder: Providing an egg-free protein source is essential for maintaining muscle health and overall nutrition in an EoE-friendly diet. Plant-based proteins such as pea or hemp are easily digestible and can be less likely to trigger EoE symptoms compared to animal-based proteins.

Nutritional Information (per serving, with almond milk and without optional toppings):

- Calories: Approximately 300-350
- Protein: 15-20g

- Total Fat: 5-10g
- Fiber: 8-10g
- Sodium: Low

Sweet Potato Toast with Avocado and Spinach

Serves: 1

Cooking Time: 25 minutes

Ingredients and Portions/Measurements:

- Sweet Potato (large): 1 (Sliced lengthwise into 1/4-inch thick slices; rich in vitamins A and C, fiber, and potassium, phase 2 reintroduction EoE diet friendly)
- Avocado: 1/2, mashed (Offers healthy fats, fiber, and essential vitamins)
- Fresh Spinach: 1/2 cup (High in iron, vitamin K, and magnesium)
- Almond Butter: 1 tablespoon (Rich in healthy fats and vitamin E; reintroduced in phase 2)
- Substitution (if almond butter triggers): Sunflower seed butter 1 tablespoon (Nut-free alternative, rich in vitamins E and B6, and magnesium)

- Chia Seeds: 1 teaspoon (For added omega-3 fatty acids and fiber)
- Salt and Pepper: To taste (Enhances flavor, use minimally)

Instructions:

- Prep Sweet Potato Toast: Preheat your oven to 400°F (200°C). Line a baking sheet with parchment paper. Place sweet potato slices on the sheet and bake for 20 minutes or until tender but still firm.
- Mash Avocado: While sweet potatoes are baking, mash half an avocado in a small bowl. Season with a little salt and pepper.
- Assemble: Once sweet potato slices are done, let them cool slightly. Spread mashed avocado over each slice. Top with fresh spinach leaves and a drizzle of almond butter (or sunflower seed butter).
- Serve: Sprinkle chia seeds over the top for extra nutrition and texture. Enjoy immediately.

Scientific Notes:

- Sweet Potato: This vegetable is a powerhouse of nutrition, providing a high amount of vitamin A, which is important for vision and immune health, as well as vitamin C and potassium. The fiber content in sweet potatoes promotes healthy digestion, making it an excellent food choice for those managing EoE.

- Almond Butter and Sunflower Seed Butter: Both are great sources of healthy fats and can be included in a diet focusing on reducing inflammation associated with EoE. Almond butter provides vitamin E, an antioxidant, while sunflower seed butter is an alternative for those with nut allergies, offering magnesium, which is essential for muscle and nerve function.
- Chia Seeds: Known for their high omega-3 fatty acid content, chia seeds can help reduce inflammation in the body, which is beneficial for individuals with EoE. They also provide additional fiber to aid in digestion.

Nutritional Information (per serving, with almond butter):

- Calories: Approximately 350-400
- Protein: 5-8g
- Total Fat: 15-20g
- Fiber: 10-12g
- Sodium: Low

Coconut Yogurt Parfait with Mixed Berries and Gluten-Free Granola

Serves: 1

Cooking Time: 5 minutes (no cooking required)

Ingredients and Portions/Measurements:

- Coconut Yogurt: 1 cup (Dairy-free, rich in probiotics, suitable for EoE diet phase 2 reintroduction)
- Mixed Berries (blueberries, raspberries, strawberries): 1/2 cup (High in antioxidants, vitamins, and fiber)
- Gluten-Free Granola: 1/4 cup (Provides texture and additional nutrients; ensure it's free of triggers)
- Honey: 1 tablespoon (For natural sweetness; if tolerated)
- Substitution (if honey triggers): Maple syrup 1 tablespoon (Another natural sweetener option, lower in fructose)
- Chia Seeds: 1 teaspoon (For added omega-3 fatty acids and fiber)

Instructions:

- Layer the Parfait: In a serving glass or bowl, start with a layer of coconut yogurt.

- Add Berries: Add a layer of mixed berries over the yogurt.
- Add Granola: Sprinkle a layer of gluten-free granola on top of the berries.
- Repeat: Repeat the layers until all ingredients are used, finishing with a few berries on top for presentation.
- Drizzle Sweetener: Drizzle honey or maple syrup over the top layer.
- Garnish: Sprinkle chia seeds over the parfait for a nutritional boost.
- Serve: Enjoy immediately for best texture and flavor.

Scientific Notes:

- Coconut Yogurt: A fantastic dairy-free alternative that can help introduce probiotics into the diet. Probiotics are beneficial for gut health, which can be particularly important for individuals with EoE managing digestive symptoms.
- Mixed Berries: Berries are an excellent source of dietary fiber, vitamins, and antioxidants. The antioxidants in berries, such as vitamin C and various polyphenols, have been shown to reduce

inflammation and oxidative stress, potentially beneficial for EoE management.

- Chia Seeds: These tiny seeds pack a significant nutritional punch, offering omega-3 fatty acids, fiber, and protein. Omega-3s are known for their anti-inflammatory properties, which can support managing EoE symptoms.

Nutritional Information (per serving, with honey):

- Calories: Approximately 250-300
- Protein: 5-10g
- Total Fat: 10-15g
- Fiber: 5-7g
- Sodium: Low

LUNCH RECIPES
REINTRODUCTION STAGE PHASE 2

Quinoa Tabbouleh with Grilled Chicken

Serves: 1

Cooking Time: 30 minutes

Ingredients and Portions/Measurements:

- Quinoa: 1/2 cup (A complete protein source, rich in fiber, vitamins, and minerals, phase 2 reintroduction EoE diet friendly)
- Water: 1 cup (For cooking quinoa)
- Chicken Breast: 1 small (Approximately 4 ounces; reintroduced in phase 2 for its high protein content)
- Substitution (if chicken triggers): Tempeh 4 ounces (A fermented soy product, high in protein and fiber, suitable for those avoiding poultry)
- Cucumber: 1/2, diced (High in hydration and fiber)
- Tomatoes: 1/2 cup, diced (Rich in vitamins C and K, and antioxidants)
- Parsley: 1/4 cup, finely chopped (A good source of vitamins A, C, and K)

- Mint: 1 tablespoon, finely chopped (Adds flavor and digestive benefits)
- Lemon Juice: 2 tablespoons (For dressing; high in vitamin C)
- Olive Oil: 1 tablespoon (For dressing; rich in monounsaturated fats and antioxidants)
- Salt and Pepper: To taste (Enhances flavor, use minimally)

Instructions:

- Cook Quinoa: Rinse quinoa under cold running water. In a pot, bring 1 cup of water to a boil. Add quinoa, reduce to a simmer, cover, and cook until quinoa is tender and water is absorbed, about 15 minutes. Let it cool.
- Grill Chicken: Season the chicken breast (or tempeh) with a little salt and pepper. Grill over medium heat until cooked through, about 6-7 minutes per side for chicken (or until tempeh is golden brown). Let it rest before slicing thinly.
- Prepare Tabbouleh: In a large bowl, combine cooled quinoa, diced cucumber, tomatoes, chopped parsley, and mint. Add the sliced chicken (or tempeh) on top.

- Dress the Tabbouleh: Whisk together lemon juice, olive oil, salt, and pepper. Drizzle over the tabbouleh and toss gently to combine.
- Serve: Enjoy immediately, or let it chill in the refrigerator for an hour to enhance the flavors.

Scientific Notes:

- Quinoa: Known for its complete protein profile, quinoa provides all nine essential amino acids necessary for good health. It's also high in fiber, which can help with digestion—a common concern for those with EoE.
- Chicken and Tempeh: Chicken is a lean protein source, important for muscle repair and maintenance. For those avoiding animal proteins, tempeh offers a high-protein, fiber-rich alternative. The fermentation process used to make tempeh can also introduce beneficial probiotics to the diet.
- Olive Oil: A cornerstone of healthy fats, olive oil is high in monounsaturated fats and antioxidants, which can help reduce inflammation associated with EoE.

Nutritional Information (per serving, with chicken):

- Calories: Approximately 450-500

- Protein: 30-35g
- Total Fat: 15-20g
- Fiber: 6-8g
- Sodium: Moderate

Zucchini Noodles with Avocado Pesto

Serves: 1

Cooking Time: 15 minutes

Ingredients and Portions/Measurements:

- Zucchini: 1 large (Spiralized into noodles; a good source of vitamins A, C, and potassium, and an excellent low-carb alternative to traditional pasta)
- Avocado: 1/2 (Provides healthy fats, fiber, and essential vitamins, suitable for EoE diet phase 2 reintroduction)
- Fresh Basil Leaves: 1/4 cup (Rich in antioxidants and provides a fresh flavor)
- Garlic: 1 clove (For flavor; if tolerated. Can omit if garlic is a known trigger)
- Substitution (if garlic triggers): A pinch of asafoetida (Adds a garlic-like flavor without the irritants found in garlic)

- Lemon Juice: 2 tablespoons (Enhances flavor and vitamin C content)
- Olive Oil: 1 tablespoon (For the pesto; a healthy fat source high in antioxidants)
- Pine Nuts: 1 tablespoon (For texture in the pesto; rich in healthy fats and vitamins)
- Substitution (if pine nuts trigger): Hemp seeds 1 tablespoon (Nut-free alternative, rich in omega-3 fatty acids and protein)
- Salt and Pepper: To taste (Adjust according to dietary needs)

Instructions:

- Prepare Zucchini Noodles: Use a spiralizer to turn the zucchini into noodles. Place in a colander, sprinkle with a little salt, and let sit to draw out excess water. Pat dry with paper towels.
- Make Avocado Pesto: In a food processor, blend the avocado, basil leaves, garlic (or asafoetida), lemon juice, olive oil, and pine nuts (or hemp seeds) until smooth. Season with salt and pepper to taste.
- Combine: Toss the zucchini noodles with the avocado pesto until well coated.

- Serve: Enjoy immediately, garnished with additional basil leaves or hemp seeds if desired.
- Scientific Notes:
- Zucchini: Zucchini is low in calories but high in essential nutrients like potassium, which can help manage blood pressure, and antioxidants that can support reducing inflammation associated with EoE.
- Avocado: High in monounsaturated fats, avocados can support heart health and reduce inflammation. They are also a good source of fiber, which is beneficial for gut health.
- Hemp Seeds: A great alternative for those with nut allergies, hemp seeds are a complete protein source and contain significant amounts of omega-3 fatty acids, known for their anti-inflammatory properties.

Nutritional Information (per serving, with hemp seeds and without garlic):

- Calories: Approximately 300-350
- Protein: 6-10g
- Total Fat: 20-25g
- Fiber: 8-10g
- Sodium: Low

Mediterranean Chickpea Salad Bowl

Serves: 1

Cooking Time: 10 minutes (No cooking required if using canned chickpeas)

Ingredients and Portions/Measurements:

- Chickpeas: 1 cup, drained and rinsed (A good source of protein, fiber, and iron, suitable for EoE diet phase 2 reintroduction)
- Cucumber: 1/2, diced (Hydrating and rich in vitamins K and C)
- Cherry Tomatoes: 1/2 cup, halved (Packed with vitamins A and C, and antioxidants)
- Red Onion: 1/4, finely chopped (Provides flavor and nutrients, including quercetin, an anti-inflammatory compound)
- Substitution (if onion triggers): Chives 1 tablespoon, chopped (For flavor without the strong compounds in onions)
- Kalamata Olives: 1/4 cup, pitted and halved (Rich in healthy fats and vitamin E)
- Feta Cheese: 1/4 cup, crumbled (Provides calcium and protein; reintroduced in phase 2)

- Substitution (if feta cheese triggers): Dairy-free cheese 1/4 cup, crumbled (A non-dairy alternative for those sensitive to dairy)
- Lemon Juice: 2 tablespoons (For dressing; adds vitamin C and enhances iron absorption from chickpeas)
- Olive Oil: 1 tablespoon (For dressing; a healthy fat source high in monounsaturated fats)
- Dried Oregano: 1 teaspoon (Adds Mediterranean flavor and has antioxidant properties)
- Salt and Pepper: To taste (Adjust according to dietary needs)

Instructions:

- Prepare Salad Base: In a large bowl, combine drained and rinsed chickpeas, diced cucumber, halved cherry tomatoes, finely chopped red onion (or chives), pitted and halved kalamata olives, and crumbled feta cheese (or dairy-free alternative).
- Make Dressing: In a small bowl, whisk together lemon juice, olive oil, dried oregano, salt, and pepper until well combined.
- Combine: Pour the dressing over the salad ingredients and toss gently to ensure everything is evenly coated.

- Serve: Transfer to a serving bowl or plate. Enjoy immediately for the freshest taste.

Scientific Notes:

- Chickpeas: Chickpeas are not only a great source of plant-based protein but also contain significant amounts of fiber, which can help with digestive health—a concern for many with EoE. The iron in chickpeas is complemented by the vitamin C from lemon juice, enhancing iron absorption.
- Feta Cheese and Dairy-free Alternative: Feta cheese provides a source of calcium and protein. For those sensitive to dairy, dairy-free cheese alternatives can offer similar textures and flavors without the lactose, often making them a suitable option during the reintroduction phase.
- Olive Oil: Known for its anti-inflammatory properties, olive oil is rich in oleic acid, a monounsaturated fat that supports heart health and may play a role in reducing inflammation associated with EoE.

Nutritional Information (per serving, with feta cheese):

- Calories: Approximately 400-450

- Protein: 15-20g
- Total Fat: 20-25g
- Fiber: 8-10g
- Sodium: Moderate

Grilled Turkey and Avocado Wrap

Serves: 1

Cooking Time: 20 minutes

Ingredients and Portions/Measurements:

- Turkey Breast: 4 oz (A lean source of protein, suitable for reintroduction in phase 2 of the EoE diet)
- Substitution (if turkey triggers): Grilled tofu 4 oz (A plant-based protein, rich in iron and calcium, for those avoiding poultry)
- Gluten-Free Tortilla Wrap: 1 (Ensure it's suitable for an EoE elimination diet and free from known triggers)
- Avocado: 1/2, mashed (Provides healthy fats and fiber)
- Baby Spinach Leaves: 1/2 cup (Rich in vitamins A, C, E, and K)
- Carrot: 1 small, grated (A good source of beta-carotene and fiber)

- Cucumber: 1/4, thinly sliced (Hydrating and provides vitamin K)
- Dairy-Free Cheese: 1/4 cup, shredded (For those who are reintroducing dairy slowly or have identified it as a trigger)
- Olive Oil: For grilling (A heart-healthy fat high in monounsaturated fatty acids)
- Lemon Juice: 1 tablespoon (To mix with avocado, adds vitamin C and flavor)
- Salt and Pepper: To taste (Adjust according to dietary needs)

Instructions:

- Prep Avocado Spread: In a small bowl, mash the avocado with lemon juice, salt, and pepper. Set aside.
- Grill Turkey or Tofu: Brush turkey breast or tofu with a little olive oil and season with salt and pepper. Grill over medium heat until the turkey is cooked through (internal temperature of 165°F) or the tofu is nicely charred on each side, about 6-7 minutes per side.
- Assemble Wrap: Lay the gluten-free tortilla on a flat surface. Spread the mashed avocado evenly across the tortilla. Add baby spinach leaves, grated carrot, sliced cucumber, and shredded dairy-free cheese.

- Add Protein: Once cooked and slightly cooled, slice the turkey or tofu and place it on the tortilla.
- Roll the Wrap: Carefully roll the tortilla, folding in the sides to enclose the fillings. If necessary, secure with a toothpick.
- Serve: Enjoy immediately, or wrap in foil for a portable lunch option.

Scientific Notes:

- Turkey and Tofu: Both turkey and tofu are excellent sources of protein, essential for muscle repair and overall health. Turkey is a lean meat option, low in fat but high in protein, making it a good choice for those monitoring fat intake. Tofu, being plant-based, offers not only protein but also a range of phytonutrients and is a viable option for those on a vegetarian or elimination diet phase.
- Avocado: Avocado is rich in monounsaturated fats, which can help reduce inflammation in the body. This is particularly beneficial for individuals with EoE, as reducing inflammation can help manage symptoms.
- Dairy-Free Cheese: Provides an alternative for those sensitive to dairy products, allowing them to enjoy the

creaminess of cheese without the potential triggers associated with dairy.

Nutritional Information (per serving, with turkey):

- Calories: Approximately 400-450
- Protein: 25-30g
- Total Fat: 20-25g
- Fiber: 6-8g
- Sodium: Moderate

Lemon Herb Salmon with Quinoa Salad

Serves: 1

Cooking Time: 25 minutes

Ingredients and Portions/Measurements:

- Salmon Fillet: 1 (4 oz, rich in omega-3 fatty acids, suitable for reintroduction in phase 2 of the EoE diet)
- Quinoa: 1/2 cup (A complete protein source, rich in fiber, vitamins, and minerals)
- Water: 1 cup (For cooking quinoa)
- Baby Spinach: 1 cup (A nutrient-dense leafy green, high in vitamins A, C, and K)
- Cherry Tomatoes: 1/2 cup, halved (Rich in vitamins C and K, and lycopene, an antioxidant)
- Cucumber: 1/2, diced (Hydrating and provides vitamin K)
- Lemon: 1/2 (For juice and zest, adds flavor and vitamin C)
- Olive Oil: 2 tablespoons (Divided for salmon and salad dressing; a healthy fat source high in monounsaturated fats)

- Fresh Herbs (dill, parsley): 1 tablespoon each, chopped (Adds flavor and nutritional benefits, including antioxidants)
- Salt and Pepper: To taste (Adjust according to dietary needs)
- Almond Milk (unsweetened): 2 tablespoons (If reintroduced successfully; for quinoa cooking if milk triggers)
- Substitution (if almond milk triggers): Water or coconut milk 2 tablespoons (For cooking quinoa, if avoiding nuts)

Instructions:

- Cook Quinoa: Rinse quinoa under cold water. In a pot, combine quinoa, water (or almond milk/coconut milk), and a pinch of salt. Bring to a boil, then cover and simmer for 15 minutes, or until all liquid is absorbed. Fluff with a fork and let cool slightly.
- Prepare Salmon: Preheat the oven to 375°F (190°C). Place the salmon on a baking sheet lined with parchment paper. Brush with 1 tablespoon olive oil, and sprinkle with lemon zest, salt, and pepper. Bake for 12-15 minutes, or until salmon flakes easily with a fork.

- Make Salad: In a bowl, combine baby spinach, halved cherry tomatoes, diced cucumber, and cooled quinoa.
- Dress the Salad: Whisk together lemon juice, the remaining olive oil, chopped fresh herbs, salt, and pepper. Drizzle over the salad and toss to combine.
- Serve: Place the quinoa salad on a plate, top with the baked salmon, and garnish with additional fresh herbs and lemon wedges if desired.

Scientific Notes:

- Salmon: A great source of omega-3 fatty acids, which are known for their anti-inflammatory properties. This can be particularly beneficial for individuals with eosinophilic esophagitis (EoE) as part of an anti-inflammatory diet strategy.
- Quinoa: This gluten-free grain (technically a seed) is a complete protein, meaning it contains all nine essential amino acids, which is rare for plant-based foods. It's also a good source of fiber, which can help support a healthy gut microbiome.
- Almond Milk/Coconut Milk: Both are dairy-free alternatives rich in vitamins and minerals. They can be used in cooking quinoa to add a creamy texture

and additional flavor without the potential issues associated with cow's milk.

Nutritional Information (per serving, with almond milk):

- Calories: Approximately 500-550
- Protein: 25-30g
- Total Fat: 25-30g
- Fiber: 6-8g
- Sodium: Low to Moderate

DINNER RECIPES

REINTRODUCTION STAGE PHASE 2

Baked Cod with Roasted Vegetables

Serves: 1

Cooking Time: 30 minutes

Ingredients and Portions/Measurements:

- Cod Fillet: 1 (6 oz, a lean source of protein, rich in omega-3 fatty acids, suitable for reintroduction in phase 2 of the EoE diet)
- Olive Oil: 2 tablespoons (Divided for fish and vegetables; a heart-healthy fat high in monounsaturated fats)
- Lemon: 1 (Half sliced, half juiced; provides vitamin C and enhances flavor)
- Zucchini: 1/2, sliced (Rich in vitamins A and C, and hydration)
- Carrots: 2 medium, peeled and sliced (A good source of beta-carotene, fiber, and vitamins)
- Bell Pepper: 1/2, sliced (Rich in vitamins C and A)

- Broccoli Florets: 1/2 cup (High in vitamins K and C, and fiber)
- Garlic Powder: 1 teaspoon (For flavor; can be adjusted based on tolerance)
- Dried Thyme: 1/2 teaspoon (Adds earthy flavor and contains antioxidants)
- Salt and Pepper: To taste (Adjust according to dietary needs)
- Almond Milk: For sauce (If reintroduced successfully; can be used to create a dairy-free lemon sauce if milk is tolerated)
- Substitution (if almond milk triggers): Coconut milk or broth for sauce (Provides a creamy texture without dairy or nuts)

Instructions:

- Preheat Oven: Preheat your oven to 400°F (200°C).
- Prepare Vegetables: Toss zucchini, carrots, bell pepper, and broccoli florets with 1 tablespoon olive oil, garlic powder, salt, and pepper. Spread them on a baking sheet in a single layer.
- Season Cod: Place the cod fillet on a piece of aluminum foil large enough to fold over and seal. Drizzle with the remaining olive oil, lemon juice,

sprinkle with dried thyme, salt, and pepper. Place lemon slices on top of the cod.

- Bake: Fold the foil around the cod to seal it. Place it on the baking sheet with the vegetables. Bake in the preheated oven for 20-25 minutes, or until the cod is flaky and vegetables are tender.

- Make Lemon Sauce (Optional): If using, gently heat almond milk (or substitution) in a saucepan, adding a squeeze of lemon juice, salt, and pepper to taste. Stir until slightly thickened.

- Serve: Carefully open the cod foil packet. Serve the baked cod alongside the roasted vegetables, drizzled with the lemon sauce if made.

Scientific Notes:

- Cod: This fish is a great source of lean protein and omega-3 fatty acids, which are essential for reducing inflammation and promoting heart health. Omega-3 fatty acids are particularly beneficial for individuals with inflammatory conditions like EoE.

- Roasted Vegetables: A mix of colorful vegetables provides a wide range of vitamins, minerals, and antioxidants. These nutrients support overall health and can help reduce inflammation in the body.

- Olive Oil: High in monounsaturated fats, olive oil is known for its heart-healthy benefits and its role in reducing inflammation, which can be beneficial for managing EoE symptoms.

Nutritional Information (per serving, without sauce):

- Calories: Approximately 400-450
- Protein: 30-35g
- Total Fat: 20-25g
- Fiber: 5-7g
- Sodium: Low to Moderate

Stuffed Bell Peppers with Ground Turkey and Vegetables

Serves: 1

Cooking Time: 45 minutes

Ingredients and Portions/Measurements:

- Bell Pepper: 1 large (Choose any color, a good source of vitamins C and A)
- Ground Turkey: 4 oz (A lean protein source, reintroduced in phase 2 for those without poultry triggers)
- Substitution (if turkey triggers): Ground chicken or a mix of mashed chickpeas for a vegetarian option
- Cooked Quinoa: 1/2 cup (Rich in protein and fiber, a good grain for those with gluten sensitivities)
- Spinach: 1/2 cup, chopped (Rich in iron and calcium)
- Mushrooms: 1/4 cup, diced (Provides selenium, potassium, and B vitamins)
- Onion: 2 tablespoons, finely chopped (Adds flavor, contains antioxidants)
- Substitution (if onion triggers): Fennel, finely chopped, for a milder flavor

- Garlic: 1 clove, minced (If tolerated; can be omitted if garlic is a known trigger)
- Olive Oil: 1 teaspoon (For cooking; a healthy fat source)
- Dried Oregano: 1/2 teaspoon (Adds Mediterranean flavor)
- Salt and Pepper: To taste (Adjust according to dietary needs)
- Dairy-Free Cheese: 2 tablespoons, shredded (For topping; can use any type tolerated or skip if cheese is not reintroduced)

Instructions:

- Preheat Oven: Preheat your oven to 375°F (190°C).
- Prepare Bell Pepper: Cut the top off the bell pepper and remove the seeds and membranes. Place the bell pepper in a baking dish.
- Cook Filling: Heat olive oil in a skillet over medium heat. Add ground turkey (or substitute), onion (or fennel), garlic, mushrooms, and cook until the meat is browned and vegetables are soft. Stir in cooked quinoa, chopped spinach, oregano, salt, and pepper. Cook for an additional 2 minutes.

- Stuff Bell Pepper: Spoon the turkey and quinoa mixture into the hollowed-out bell pepper. Top with dairy-free cheese if using.
- Bake: Cover with aluminum foil and bake for about 30 minutes. Uncover and bake for another 15 minutes, or until the bell pepper is tender and the cheese is melted and slightly browned.
- Serve: Let it cool for a few minutes before serving. Enjoy your nutritious and filling stuffed bell pepper.

Scientific Notes:

- Bell Pepper: High in vitamin C, which can help with the absorption of iron from the spinach, and vitamin A, important for immune function and eye health.
- Ground Turkey: Provides a lean source of protein, important for muscle repair and overall health. For those avoiding meat, chickpeas offer a fiber-rich protein alternative that can support gut health.
- Quinoa: A complete protein, providing all nine essential amino acids, and a good source of fiber, both important for maintaining a healthy digestive system in individuals with EoE.

Nutritional Information (per serving, with ground turkey and dairy-free cheese):

- Calories: Approximately 350-400
- Protein: 25-30g
- Total Fat: 10-15g
- Fiber: 5-7g
- Sodium: Moderate

Eggplant and Lentil Curry

Serves: 1

Cooking Time: 40 minutes

Ingredients and Portions/Measurements:

- Eggplant: 1 small (cut into cubes, a good source of fiber and antioxidants)
- Red Lentils: 1/2 cup (rich in protein, fiber, and iron, suitable for reintroduction in phase 2 of the EoE diet)
- Coconut Milk: 1 cup (a dairy-free alternative, rich in vitamins and minerals)
- Substitution (if coconut milk triggers): Oat milk 1 cup (another dairy-free alternative, rich in fiber)
- Tomato Paste: 1 tablespoon (concentrated source of lycopene, a powerful antioxidant)
- Onion: 1/4 cup, finely chopped (adds flavor, contains quercetin, an anti-inflammatory compound)
- Substitution (if onion triggers): Asafoetida powder 1/4 teaspoon (adds onion-like flavor without the allergens)
- Garlic: 1 clove, minced (if tolerated; can be omitted if garlic is a known trigger)

- Ginger: 1 teaspoon, grated (anti-inflammatory properties and adds flavor)
- Curry Powder: 1 teaspoon (a blend of spices, each with its own health benefits)
- Spinach: 1 cup (rich in iron and calcium)
- Olive Oil: 1 teaspoon (for sautéing; a healthy fat source)
- Salt and Pepper: To taste (adjust according to dietary needs)

Instructions:

- Prepare Ingredients: Preheat a large pan over medium heat. Add olive oil, onion (or asafoetida), garlic, and ginger. Sauté until the onion is translucent and fragrant.
- Cook Eggplant: Add the cubed eggplant to the pan and cook until it begins to soften, about 5 minutes.
- Add Lentils: Stir in the red lentils, tomato paste, and curry powder until well combined.
- Add Liquid: Pour in the coconut milk (or oat milk) and bring the mixture to a simmer. Reduce the heat to low, cover, and let it cook for about 25 minutes, or until the lentils are soft and the curry has thickened.

- Add Spinach: Stir in the spinach and cook until it wilts, about 2 minutes.
- Season: Taste and adjust the seasoning with salt and pepper.
- Serve: Enjoy your eggplant and lentil curry warm, as a hearty and nutritious meal.

Scientific Notes:

- Eggplant: Contains nasunin, a type of antioxidant that may help protect brain cell membranes.
- Red Lentils: A great source of plant-based protein and dietary fiber, which can support digestive health. The iron in lentils is also important for those on a vegetarian diet.
- Coconut Milk: Provides medium-chain triglycerides (MCTs), which are easily absorbed for quick energy. Oat milk can be a good alternative for those with nut allergies or sensitivities to coconut.
- Curry Powder: Spices in curry powder, like turmeric, can have anti-inflammatory and antioxidant properties, beneficial for managing conditions like EoE.

Nutritional Information (per serving, with coconut milk):

- Calories: Approximately 450-500
- Protein: 18-22g
- Total Fat: 20-25g
- Fiber: 15-20g
- Sodium: Moderate

Thai Basil Turkey Stir-Fry

Serves: 1

Cooking Time: 20 minutes

Ingredients and Portions/Measurements:

- Ground Turkey: 4 oz (A lean protein source, reintroduced in phase 2 for those without poultry triggers)
- Substitution (if turkey triggers): Ground tempeh 4 oz (A plant-based protein, rich in probiotics and nutrients, suitable for those avoiding poultry)
- Thai Basil Leaves: 1/2 cup (Provides a unique flavor and antioxidants)
- Bell Pepper: 1/2, sliced (Rich in vitamins C and A)
- Carrot: 1 small, julienned (A good source of beta-carotene and fiber)
- Green Beans: 1/2 cup, trimmed (Rich in fiber and vitamins K and C)
- Coconut Aminos: 2 tablespoons (A soy-free alternative to soy sauce, lower in sodium)
- Garlic: 1 clove, minced (If tolerated; can be omitted if garlic is a known trigger)

- Ginger: 1 teaspoon, grated (Anti-inflammatory properties and adds flavor)
- Olive Oil or Coconut Oil: 1 tablespoon (For stir-frying; healthy fat sources)
- Red Chili Flakes: 1/4 teaspoon (For heat; adjust to taste or omit if sensitive)
- Lime: 1 (Juice added for flavor and vitamin C; garnish with a wedge)
- Salt and Pepper: To taste (Adjust according to dietary needs)

Instructions:

- Prepare Ingredients: Have all your vegetables cut and ready. Mix coconut aminos, lime juice, and red chili flakes in a small bowl to make the sauce.
- Cook Protein: Heat oil in a large skillet or wok over medium-high heat. Add ground turkey (or tempeh) and cook until browned, breaking it into small pieces as it cooks.
- Sauté Vegetables: Add the minced garlic (if using) and grated ginger to the skillet and sauté for about 1 minute until fragrant. Add the bell pepper, carrot, and green beans, and stir-fry for another 3-5 minutes until just tender.

- Combine: Pour the sauce mixture over the cooked turkey and vegetables. Add the Thai basil leaves and stir everything together until the basil is wilted and everything is well coated in the sauce.
- Finish and Serve: Season with salt and pepper to taste. Serve the stir-fry hot, garnished with a lime wedge for an extra burst of flavor.

Scientific Notes:

- Ground Turkey/Tempeh: Both are excellent sources of protein. Turkey is low in fat and high in protein, while tempeh is rich in probiotics, aiding in gut health, making them both suitable for different dietary needs in the EoE reintroduction phase.
- Thai Basil: Offers not only a distinctive flavor but also contains compounds that have antioxidant and anti-inflammatory properties, potentially beneficial for managing EoE symptoms.
- Coconut Aminos: A healthier, lower-sodium alternative to traditional soy sauce, making it a suitable option for those on restricted diets or with soy sensitivities.

Nutritional Information (per serving, with ground turkey):

- Calories: Approximately 350-400
- Protein: 20-25g
- Total Fat: 10-15g
- Fiber: 4-6g
- Sodium: Low to Moderate

Roasted Butternut Squash and Chickpea Soup

Serves: 1

Cooking Time: 45 minutes

Ingredients and Portions/Measurements:

- Butternut Squash: 1 cup, cubed (High in vitamins A and C, fiber, and potassium)
- Chickpeas: 1/2 cup, drained and rinsed (Rich in protein, fiber, and iron, suitable for reintroduction in phase 2)
- Vegetable Broth: 2 cups (Choose a low-sodium option to control salt intake)
- Coconut Milk: 1/4 cup (A dairy-free alternative, adds creaminess. Use light coconut milk for less fat)
- Substitution (if coconut milk triggers): Almond milk 1/4 cup (Another dairy-free alternative, ensure it's unsweetened)
- Olive Oil: 1 tablespoon (For roasting vegetables, provides healthy fats)
- Onion: 2 tablespoons, finely chopped (Adds flavor, contains antioxidants)

- Substitution (if onion triggers): A pinch of asafoetida powder (Adds a similar flavor without the allergens)
- Garlic: 1 clove, minced (If tolerated; can be omitted if garlic is a known trigger)
- Cumin: 1/2 teaspoon (Adds warmth and depth to the soup)
- Paprika: 1/4 teaspoon (For a hint of smokiness)
- Salt and Pepper: To taste (Adjust according to dietary needs)

Instructions:

- Roast Vegetables: Preheat the oven to 400°F (200°C). Toss the cubed butternut squash and chickpeas with olive oil, salt, and pepper on a baking sheet. Roast for 25-30 minutes until the squash is tender and chickpeas are slightly crispy.
- Sauté Base: In a large pot, heat a drizzle of olive oil over medium heat. Add the chopped onion (or asafoetida) and minced garlic, sautéing until soft and fragrant. Stir in the cumin and paprika, cooking for another minute.
- Simmer Soup: Add the roasted butternut squash and chickpeas to the pot along with the vegetable broth.

Bring to a simmer and cook for 10 minutes, allowing the flavors to meld.

- Blend Soup: Carefully blend the soup using an immersion blender (or transfer to a blender) until smooth. If the soup is too thick, add a bit more broth to reach your desired consistency.

- Finish with Coconut Milk: Stir in the coconut milk (or almond milk) and heat through. Season with salt and pepper to taste.

- Serve: Pour the soup into a bowl. Garnish with a swirl of coconut milk, a sprinkle of paprika, or fresh herbs if desired. Enjoy warm.

Scientific Notes:

- Butternut Squash: Rich in beta-carotene, which the body converts into vitamin A, essential for immune function, eye health, and skin integrity. Its high fiber content can also support digestive health.

- Chickpeas: Provide plant-based protein and fiber, supporting muscle health and digestive function. They are also a good source of iron, which is important for those on a vegetarian diet or with EoE to prevent anemia.

- Coconut Milk: Offers medium-chain triglycerides (MCTs), which are metabolized differently than other fats and can provide a quick source of energy.

Nutritional Information (per serving, with coconut milk):

- Calories: Approximately 300-350
- Protein: 8-10g
- Total Fat: 10-15g
- Fiber: 6-8g
- Sodium: Low to Moderate

7 DAYS MEAL PLAN FOR REINTRODUCTION PHASE 2

Day 1

Breakfast: Fluffy Almond Milk and Chia Pancakes

Lunch: Quinoa Tabbouleh with Grilled Chicken

Dinner: Baked Cod with Roasted Vegetables

Day 2

Breakfast: Avocado and Quinoa Breakfast Bowl

Lunch: Zucchini Noodles with Avocado Pesto

Dinner: Stuffed Bell Peppers with Ground Turkey and Vegetables

Day 3

Breakfast: Berry Smoothie Bowl with Egg-Free Protein

Lunch: Mediterranean Chickpea Salad Bowl

Dinner: Eggplant and Lentil Curry

Day 4

Breakfast: Sweet Potato Toast with Avocado and Spinach

Lunch: Grilled Turkey and Avocado Wrap

Dinner: Thai Basil Turkey Stir-Fry

Day 5

Breakfast: Coconut Yogurt Parfait with Mixed Berries and Gluten-Free Granola

Lunch: Lemon Herb Salmon with Quinoa Salad

Dinner: Roasted Butternut Squash and Chickpea Soup

Day 6

Breakfast: Fluffy Almond Milk and Chia Pancakes

Lunch: Zucchini Noodles with Avocado Pesto

Dinner: Eggplant and Lentil Curry

Day 7

Breakfast: Berry Smoothie Bowl with Egg-Free Protein

Lunch: Quinoa Tabbouleh with Grilled Chicken

Dinner: Stuffed Bell Peppers with Ground Turkey and Vegetables

MEAL PLANNER

AMOS JIMMY
DAILY MEAL PLANNER

DATE _____   M T W T F S S
:

BREAKFAST   **DINNER**

LUNCH

NOTES

SNACKS

JIMMY'S CULINARY HAVEN

Looking Ahead to Phase 3: Stepping into Maintenance

The Maintenance Stage is where your journey culminates in a tailored diet that accommodates your unique dietary needs, ensuring long-term management of your condition. By this stage, you've gained a deep understanding of which foods you can enjoy freely and those you need to avoid. This phase empowers you to maintain a balanced, varied diet that supports your health and enables you to lead a fulfilling lifestyle without compromising your dietary well-being.

Throughout this journey, we encourage you to remain proactive in managing your diet, experimenting with new recipes and foods within your tolerance levels, and staying informed about the latest EoE dietary research. Your active participation is essential in maintaining the quality of life you deserve, and we're here to support you every step of the way.

We appreciate your commitment to navigating these dietary stages with an open mind and a focus on your health. Your insights and experiences are invaluable, helping us refine our approach and support others in the EoE community more effectively. As you continue to progress through these phases, we look forward to your feedback and success stories, celebrating each milestone you achieve in your dietary journey.

CHAPTER 4

BREAKFAST RECIPES
MAINTENANCE PHASE 3

*Sweet Potato and Black Bean Breakfast
Burrito*

Serves: 1

Cooking Time: 30 minutes

Ingredients and Portions/Measurements:

- Sweet Potato: 1/2 cup, cubed (Rich in beta-carotene, vitamins A and C, and fiber)
- Black Beans: 1/2 cup, drained and rinsed (High in protein and fiber, suitable for phase 3 maintenance EoE diet)
- Spinach: 1/2 cup, fresh (Packed with iron, magnesium, and vitamins A, C, and K)
- Gluten-Free Tortilla: 1 (Ensure it's free from triggers identified during the reintroduction phase)
- Avocado: 1/4, sliced (Provides healthy fats, fiber, and potassium)

- Tomato: 1/4 cup, diced (Source of vitamins C, K, and potassium)
- Olive Oil: 1 teaspoon (For cooking sweet potato; a heart-healthy fat)
- Cumin Powder: 1/4 teaspoon (Adds a warm, earthy flavor and contains antioxidants)
- Chili Powder: 1/8 teaspoon (Adds heat and flavor, contains capsaicin for anti-inflammatory properties)
- Salt and Pepper: To taste (Adjust according to dietary needs)
- Dairy-Free Cheese: 2 tablespoons, shredded (Optional, if reintroduced successfully or if a non-dairy substitute is preferred)

Instructions:

- Roast Sweet Potato: Preheat the oven to 400°F (200°C). Toss cubed sweet potato with olive oil, cumin, chili powder, salt, and pepper. Spread on a baking sheet and roast for 20 minutes, or until tender.
- Prepare Filling: In a bowl, combine roasted sweet potato, rinsed black beans, diced tomato, and fresh spinach. Gently mix to combine.
- Assemble Burrito: Lay the gluten-free tortilla flat on a plate. Spread the sweet potato and black bean mixture

in the center. Add sliced avocado and sprinkle with dairy-free cheese, if using.

- Roll Burrito: Fold in the sides of the tortilla, then roll tightly from the bottom up to encase the filling.
- Serve: Enjoy as is, or lightly grill on a pan for a crispy exterior. Serve with a side of salsa or guacamole if desired.

Scientific Notes:

- Sweet Potato: The high beta-carotene content in sweet potatoes is converted to vitamin A in the body, which is essential for immune function and eye health. Its fiber content supports healthy digestion.
- Black Beans: A great plant-based protein source, black beans are also rich in fiber, which can aid in maintaining a healthy gut microbiome, particularly beneficial for those with EoE.
- Spinach and Avocado: Both are nutrient-dense foods that provide a wide range of vitamins and minerals. Spinach is an excellent source of iron and magnesium, while avocado offers healthy monounsaturated fats and fiber, contributing to heart health and overall dietary balance.

Nutritional Information (per serving, without dairy-free cheese):

- Calories: Approximately 350-400
- Protein: 10-15g
- Total Fat: 10-15g
- Fiber: 10-12g
- Sodium: Moderate

Coconut Rice Porridge with Fruit Compote

Serves: 1

Cooking Time: 25 minutes

Ingredients and Portions/Measurements:

- Brown Rice: 1/2 cup, cooked (High in fiber, suitable for Phase 3 maintenance EOE diet)
- Substitution for milk trigger: Use coconut milk instead of dairy milk for cooking the porridge
- Coconut Milk: 3/4 cup (For cooking the rice into porridge; a rich, dairy-free alternative providing healthy fats)
- Cinnamon Stick: 1 (Adds flavor and has anti-inflammatory properties)
- Mixed Berries: 1/2 cup (Blueberries, raspberries, and strawberries - high in antioxidants and vitamin C)
- Chia Seeds: 1 tablespoon (Rich in omega-3 fatty acids, fiber, and calcium)
- Honey or Maple Syrup: 1 tablespoon (For sweetness, adjust according to taste)
- Substitution for honey if vegan: Use maple syrup or agave syrup

- Flaxseed Meal (Optional for Egg Trigger): 1 tablespoon mixed with 2.5 tablespoons of water, let sit for 5 minutes (Can act as a binder and provide omega-3 fatty acids, if eggs are a concern)

Instructions:

- Prepare Porridge: In a small saucepan, combine the cooked brown rice with coconut milk and a cinnamon stick. Cook over medium heat, stirring occasionally, until the mixture thickens to your desired consistency, about 15-20 minutes. Remove the cinnamon stick before serving.
- Make Fruit Compote: While the porridge is cooking, heat the mixed berries in a separate small saucepan over low heat. Add a splash of water and honey (or maple syrup) and let simmer until the berries break down slightly and the mixture becomes syrupy, about 5-10 minutes.
- Assemble: Pour the thickened rice porridge into a bowl. Top with the warm berry compote.
- Add Toppings: Sprinkle chia seeds over the top. If using, add the prepared flaxseed meal mixture as an additional topping for extra omega-3s and fiber.

- Serve Warm: Enjoy this comforting, nutrient-packed breakfast warm, perfect for starting the day right on a maintenance phase of an EoE diet.

Scientific Note:

- This breakfast option is designed to be gentle on the esophagus while providing a high nutritional value. The use of coconut milk instead of dairy milk caters to those who have identified dairy as a trigger. Brown rice and chia seeds contribute dietary fiber, which is essential for digestive health, and the mixed berries offer a good dose of antioxidants, supporting overall wellness.

Nutritional Information (per serving, without flaxseed meal):

- Calories: ~300-350
- Protein: 5-7g
- Total Fat: 14-17g (primarily from avocado and chia seeds)
- Fiber: 6-8g
- Sodium: Low

Savory Oatmeal with Sautéed Vegetables

Serves: 1

Cooking Time: 20 minutes

Ingredients and Portions/Measurements:

- Rolled Oats: 1/2 cup (Rich in fiber, supports digestive health, Phase 3 maintenance EOE diet friendly)
- Water or Vegetable Broth: 1 cup (For cooking oats; use broth for more flavor)
- Zucchini: 1/4 cup, diced (Low allergenic potential, high in vitamins B6, riboflavin, and minerals)
- Bell Pepper: 1/4 cup, diced (Vitamin C rich, tolerated by many patients, enhances immune function)
- Spinach: 1/4 cup, roughly chopped (Iron and magnesium source, Phase 3 maintenance EOE diet friendly)
- Olive Oil: 1 teaspoon (For sautéing vegetables; healthy fat source)
- Nutritional Yeast: 1 tablespoon (Cheesy flavor without dairy, B-vitamins rich)
- Substitution (if nutritional yeast triggers): Hemp seeds 1 tablespoon (For a nutty flavor and omega-3s)

- Avocado: 1/4, sliced (Healthy fats, fiber, Phase 3 maintenance EOE diet friendly)
- Salt and Pepper: To taste (Adjust based on dietary needs and tolerances)

Instructions:

- Cook Oatmeal: In a small pot, bring water or vegetable broth to a boil. Add rolled oats and reduce heat to simmer. Cook, stirring occasionally, until oats are soft and have absorbed most of the liquid, about 5-10 minutes.
- Sauté Vegetables: While oats are cooking, heat olive oil in a pan over medium heat. Add diced zucchini and bell pepper, sautéing until just tender, about 5 minutes. Add spinach in the last minute of cooking until wilted.
- Assemble Bowl: Transfer cooked oatmeal to a bowl. Stir in nutritional yeast (or hemp seeds) for a cheesy or nutty flavor.
- Top with Vegetables and Avocado: Spoon the sautéed vegetables over the oatmeal. Top with sliced avocado.
- Season: Season with salt and pepper to taste. Serve warm.

Scientific Note:

This savory oatmeal recipe is designed with the EOE diet in mind, incorporating ingredients that are generally well-tolerated and nutrient-rich to support overall health. Oats are an excellent source of soluble fiber, beneficial for digestive health. The inclusion of vegetables increases the meal's vitamin and mineral content, particularly vitamins C and B6, iron, and magnesium, supporting immune function and energy levels. Nutritional yeast (or hemp seeds) adds B-vitamins (or omega-3 fatty acids), enhancing the nutritional profile of the dish without introducing common allergens.

Nutritional Information (per serving, with water):

- Calories: ~300-350
- Protein: 8-10g
- Total Fat: 14-16g
- Fiber: 7-9g
- Sodium: Low to Moderate

Pumpkin Seed Pesto Zoodles with Poached Chicken

Serves: 1

Cooking Time: 30 minutes

Ingredients and Portions/Measurements:

- Zucchini: 1 large, spiralized (Rich in vitamins A and C, low allergenic potential, supports digestive health)
- Chicken Breast: 4 oz, cooked and shredded (Lean protein source, Phase 3 maintenance EoE diet-friendly)
- Substitution (if chicken triggers): Tofu 4 oz, pressed and cubed (Plant-based protein, rich in calcium and iron)
- Pumpkin Seeds: 2 tablespoons, toasted (Magnesium-rich, for making pesto)
- Fresh Basil Leaves: 1/4 cup (For pesto; anti-inflammatory properties)
- Garlic: 1 clove, minced (If tolerated; can be omitted or substituted with garlic-infused oil for flavor)
- Olive Oil: 2 tablespoons (For pesto; healthy fat source)

- Lemon Juice: 1 tablespoon (Adds brightness and vitamin C to the pesto)
- Nutritional Yeast: 1 teaspoon (Adds a cheesy flavor without dairy; B-vitamins rich)
- Substitution (if nutritional yeast triggers): Additional lemon zest for flavor enhancement
- Salt and Pepper: To taste (Adjust based on dietary needs and tolerances)

Instructions:

- Prepare Zoodles: Spiralize the zucchini into noodles (zoodles). Set aside in a colander to drain any excess moisture.
- Cook Chicken: Poach the chicken breast in simmering water until fully cooked, about 12-15 minutes. Once cooled, shred the chicken using forks. For the tofu option, pan-fry cubed tofu in a teaspoon of olive oil until golden on all sides.
- Make Pumpkin Seed Pesto: In a food processor, combine toasted pumpkin seeds, basil leaves, minced garlic (if using), olive oil, lemon juice, nutritional yeast (or lemon zest), and a pinch of salt and pepper. Process until smooth.

- Combine Zoodles and Pesto: Toss the zoodles with the pumpkin seed pesto until well coated. You can do this in a sauté pan over low heat to warm through if desired.
- Assemble Bowl: Place the pesto zoodles in a bowl. Top with shredded chicken or tofu.
- Serve: Adjust seasoning with salt and pepper. Serve immediately, garnished with extra pumpkin seeds or fresh basil leaves if desired.

Scientific Note:

This recipe caters to the EoE maintenance phase, focusing on easily digestible and non-triggering ingredients. Zucchini is gentle on the digestive system, while pumpkin seeds offer magnesium, known for its muscle-relaxing properties. Basil provides anti-inflammatory benefits, crucial for managing EoE symptoms. This meal is designed to provide balanced nutrition, emphasizing ingredients that support overall wellness and digestive health without compromising flavor.

Nutritional Information (per serving, with chicken):

- Calories: ~350-400
- Protein: 25-30g

- Total Fat: 18-22g
- Fiber: 3-5g
- Sodium: Moderate

Pear and Walnut Oat Bran Bowl

Serves: 1

Cooking Time: 15 minutes

Ingredients and Portions/Measurements:

- Oat Bran: 1/2 cup (High in fiber, supports digestive health, beneficial for Phase 3 maintenance EOE diet)
- Almond Milk: 1 cup (Dairy-free alternative, rich in vitamin E)
- Substitution (if almond milk triggers): Rice milk 1 cup (Another dairy-free alternative, gentle on the stomach)
- Pear: 1 medium, diced (Rich in fiber and vitamin C, easily digestible fruit)
- Walnuts: 2 tablespoons, chopped (Good source of omega-3 fatty acids and antioxidants)
- Substitution (if walnuts trigger): Pumpkin seeds 2 tablespoons (Nut-free source of omega-3s and minerals)

- Cinnamon: 1/2 teaspoon (Anti-inflammatory properties and adds flavor)
- Maple Syrup: 1 teaspoon (Natural sweetener, adds a subtle sweetness)
- Ground Flaxseed: 1 tablespoon (Rich in omega-3 fatty acids and fiber, if no triggers)

Instructions:

- Cook Oat Bran: In a medium saucepan, bring almond milk (or rice milk) to a boil. Stir in oat bran and reduce heat to medium-low. Cook for about 5-7 minutes, stirring occasionally, until the bran thickens.
- Add Flavors: Once the oat bran is cooked, stir in the diced pear, cinnamon, and maple syrup. Cook for an additional 2 minutes, allowing the pear to soften slightly.
- Prepare Toppings: If using walnuts (or pumpkin seeds), lightly toast them in a dry pan over medium heat for 2-3 minutes, stirring frequently to prevent burning.
- Assemble Bowl: Spoon the cooked oat bran into a bowl. Top with toasted walnuts (or pumpkin seeds) and a sprinkle of ground flaxseed for extra fiber and omega-3s.

- Serve Warm: Enjoy your nourishing Pear and Walnut Oat Bran Bowl warm, perfect for a cozy and healthy start to your day.

Scientific Note:

This breakfast option is crafted with EoE dietary considerations in mind, focusing on ingredients known for their nutritional benefits and lower allergenic potential. Oat bran serves as an excellent fiber source, aiding in digestion. Pears are chosen for their gentle nature on the digestive system, and walnuts (or pumpkin seeds) provide healthy fats important for cognitive and cardiovascular health. This combination ensures a balanced, nutrient-rich meal suitable for the maintenance phase of an EoE diet, with easy substitutions for individual dietary needs.

Nutritional Information (per serving, with almond milk and walnuts):

- Calories: ~350-400
- Protein: 8-10g
- Total Fat: 15-18g
- Fiber: 9-11g
- Sodium: Low

LUNCH RECIPES

MAINTENANCE PHASE 3

Mediterranean Quinoa Salad with Lemon-Tahini Dressing

Serves: 1

Cooking Time: 20 minutes

Ingredients and Portions/Measurements:

- Quinoa: 1/2 cup, uncooked (A complete protein source, rich in fiber, supports digestive health, Phase 3 maintenance EoE diet friendly)
- Cherry Tomatoes: 1/4 cup, halved (Low allergenic potential, high in vitamins C and K)
- Cucumber: 1/4 cup, diced (Hydrating, contains antioxidants)
- Red Onion: 1 tablespoon, finely chopped (Enhances flavor, rich in quercetin)
- Substitution (if red onion triggers): Green onions (scallions) 1 tablespoon, green parts only (Milder in flavor, generally well-tolerated)

- Kalamata Olives: 1 tablespoon, pitted and sliced (Rich in healthy fats and vitamin E)
- Tahini: 1 tablespoon (Sesame seed paste, high in calcium and healthy fats)
- Lemon Juice: 2 tablespoons (For dressing, adds vitamin C and flavor)
- Garlic Powder: 1/4 teaspoon (If tolerated; can omit or substitute with a dash of garlic-infused olive oil for flavor without the actual garlic)
- Parsley: 1 tablespoon, chopped (Adds freshness and is a good source of vitamin K)
- Salt and Pepper: To taste (Adjust according to dietary needs and preferences)

Instructions:

- Cook Quinoa: Rinse quinoa under cold running water. In a medium saucepan, combine quinoa with 1 cup of water. Bring to a boil, then cover and simmer for 15 minutes, or until all water is absorbed. Let it cool.
- Prepare Vegetables: While quinoa is cooking, prepare the cherry tomatoes, cucumber, red onion (or green onions), and kalamata olives.
- Make Lemon-Tahini Dressing: In a small bowl, whisk together tahini, lemon juice, garlic powder (or garlic-

infused olive oil), salt, and pepper. Adjust the consistency with a little water if it's too thick.

- Assemble Salad: In a large bowl, combine cooled quinoa, prepared vegetables, and parsley. Drizzle with the lemon-tahini dressing and toss to combine.
- Serve: Enjoy your Mediterranean Quinoa Salad immediately, or chill in the refrigerator for a refreshing lunch option.

Scientific Note:

This Mediterranean Quinoa Salad is crafted with EoE dietary considerations in mind, prioritizing ingredients known for their low allergenic potential and nutritional benefits. Quinoa serves as a gluten-free grain alternative, rich in both fiber and complete protein. The inclusion of raw vegetables like cherry tomatoes and cucumbers provides essential vitamins and hydration, while the lemon-tahini dressing offers a healthy fat source, enhancing the absorption of fat-soluble vitamins. This combination ensures a balanced, nutrient-rich meal suitable for the maintenance phase of an EoE diet.

Nutritional Information (per serving):

- Calories: ~350-400

- Protein: 8-10g
- Total Fat: 12-15g
- Fiber: 5-7g
- Sodium: Moderate

Cucumber Noodle Salad with Sunflower Seed Dressing

Serves: 1

Cooking Time: 15 minutes

Ingredients and Portions/Measurements:

- Cucumber: 1 large, spiralized (Hydration and vitamin K, low allergenic potential)
- Carrot: 1/2 medium, spiralized or grated (Beta-carotene and fiber)
- Red Cabbage: 1/4 cup, thinly sliced (Vitamins A, C, and antioxidants)
- Sunflower Seeds: 2 tablespoons (for dressing; rich in vitamin E and magnesium)
- Substitution (if sunflower seeds trigger): Toasted sesame seeds 1 tablespoon (for dressing; rich in calcium and zinc)

- Olive Oil: 1 tablespoon (for dressing; healthy monounsaturated fats)
- Apple Cider Vinegar: 1 tablespoon (for dressing; digestive health benefits)
- Honey: 1 teaspoon (natural sweetener, optional)
- Substitution (if honey triggers): Pure maple syrup 1 teaspoon
- Fresh Dill: 1 tablespoon, chopped (digestive benefits and fresh flavor)
- Salt and Pepper: To taste

Instructions:

- Prepare Vegetables: Use a spiralizer to turn the cucumber and carrot into noodles. If you don't have a spiralizer, use a peeler or grater for the carrot. Thinly slice the red cabbage.
- Make Sunflower Seed Dressing: In a blender, combine sunflower seeds (or sesame seeds), olive oil, apple cider vinegar, honey (or maple syrup), fresh dill, and a pinch of salt and pepper. Blend until smooth. Add a bit of water if needed to reach your desired consistency.
- Combine Salad: In a large bowl, mix together the cucumber noodles, carrot, and red cabbage. Pour the

sunflower seed dressing over the salad and toss to coat evenly.

- Serve: Enjoy this fresh cucumber noodle salad immediately, garnished with additional dill or sunflower seeds if desired.

Scientific Note:

This salad is crafted with ingredients suitable for those in the maintenance phase of an EoE diet. Cucumbers, carrots, and red cabbage are generally well-tolerated and provide a range of vitamins, minerals, and fiber, supporting overall health and digestion. The sunflower seed dressing offers a dairy and egg-free alternative to traditional dressings, packed with healthy fats and nutrients. This recipe focuses on fresh, whole foods to minimize the risk of triggering EoE symptoms.

Nutritional Information (per serving):

Calories: ~250-300

Protein: 4-6g

Total Fat: 14-18g

Fiber: 3-5g

- Sodium: Low to Moderate

Lemon Herb Quinoa with Grilled Vegetables

Serves: 1

Cooking Time: 30 minutes

Ingredients and Portions/Measurements:

- Quinoa: 1/2 cup, uncooked (Excellent source of plant-based protein, rich in fiber, suitable for Phase 3 maintenance EOE diet)
- Vegetable Broth: 1 cup (For cooking quinoa; adds flavor without fat or dairy)
- Asparagus: 1/4 cup, trimmed (Low in allergens, high in fiber, and a good source of vitamins A, C, and E)
- Cherry Tomatoes: 1/4 cup, halved (Rich in antioxidants, including lycopene, vitamin C, and potassium)
- Yellow Bell Pepper: 1/4 cup, sliced (High in vitamin C and beta-carotene with a sweet flavor)
- Lemon Juice: 2 tablespoons (For dressing the quinoa; vitamin C source)
- Olive Oil: 1 teaspoon (For grilling vegetables; contains healthy monounsaturated fats)

- Fresh Basil: 1 tablespoon, chopped (For adding to quinoa; provides a fresh flavor and digestive benefits)
- Salt and Pepper: To taste

Instructions:

- Cook Quinoa: Rinse quinoa under cold running water to remove its natural coating, saponin, which can make it taste bitter or soapy. Bring 1 cup of vegetable broth to a boil in a medium saucepan. Add the quinoa, reduce heat to low, cover, and simmer for 15-20 minutes, or until all water is absorbed. Remove from heat and let it sit covered for 5 minutes. Fluff with a fork.
- Grill Vegetables: While the quinoa is cooking, preheat a grill pan over medium heat. Toss asparagus, cherry tomatoes, and yellow bell pepper with olive oil and a pinch of salt and pepper. Grill the vegetables until they're tender and slightly charred, about 5-7 minutes, turning occasionally.
- Prepare Lemon Herb Dressing: In a small bowl, whisk together lemon juice, a drizzle of olive oil, chopped basil, salt, and pepper.

- Assemble: Combine the cooked quinoa and grilled vegetables in a serving bowl. Drizzle with the lemon herb dressing and toss to combine.
- Serve: Enjoy your Lemon Herb Quinoa with Grilled Vegetables warm or at room temperature.

Scientific Note:

This recipe is designed with EoE dietary considerations in mind, focusing on whole, minimally processed ingredients known for their low allergenic potential and nutritional benefits. Quinoa is a versatile, gluten-free grain (technically a seed) that's a complete protein, providing all nine essential amino acids. Grilling vegetables preserves their nutrients and enhances flavor without needing heavy sauces or dressings. Lemon and basil not only add zest and freshness but also aid digestion and provide additional antioxidants, making this meal both nutritious and flavorful.

Nutritional Information (approximate, per serving):

- Calories: ~350-400
- Protein: 10-12g
- Total Fat: 9-12g
- Fiber: 5-7g

- Sodium: Moderate

Chilled Avocado Soup with Tomato Relish

Serves: 1

Cooking Time: 10 minutes (plus chilling time)

Ingredients and Portions/Measurements:

- Avocado: 1 large, ripe (Healthy fats, vitamin E, Phase 3 maintenance EOE diet friendly)
- Cucumber: 1/2 medium, peeled and chopped (Hydration and vitamin K)
- Lime Juice: 2 tablespoons (Vitamin C and freshness)
- Fresh Cilantro: 1 tablespoon, chopped (Flavor without the need for salt)
- Substitution (if cilantro triggers): Fresh parsley 1 tablespoon (Mild flavor, good for digestion)
- Garlic: 1 clove, minced (Optional, based on tolerance)
- Coconut Milk: 1/4 cup (Creaminess without dairy, rich in medium-chain triglycerides)
- Substitution (if coconut triggers): Almond milk 1/4 cup (for a lighter consistency)
- Cherry Tomatoes: 1/4 cup, diced (For the relish; rich in antioxidants)

- Red Onion: 1 tablespoon, finely chopped (For the relish; boosts flavor, contains quercetin)
- Substitution (if red onion triggers): Chives 1 tablespoon (for the relish; milder taste)
- Salt and Pepper: To taste

Instructions:

- Blend Soup: In a blender, combine the ripe avocado, cucumber, lime juice, cilantro (or parsley), garlic (if using), and coconut milk (or almond milk). Blend until smooth. Season with salt and pepper to taste. If the soup is too thick, you can thin it with a little water.
- Chill: Pour the soup into a bowl and chill in the refrigerator for at least 1 hour, or until cold.
- Prepare Tomato Relish: While the soup is chilling, mix together the diced cherry tomatoes and red onion (or chives) in a small bowl. Season with a pinch of salt and a squeeze of lime juice.
- Serve: Once chilled, give the soup a good stir, taste for seasoning, and adjust if necessary. Spoon the tomato relish over the top of the soup before serving.

Scientific Note:

This recipe offers a nutrient-dense, cooling option suitable for the maintenance phase of an EoE diet. Avocados provide beneficial monounsaturated fats, which can help reduce inflammation. The inclusion of cucumber adds hydration and additional vitamins, while lime juice and fresh herbs contribute antioxidants and enhance flavor without the need for added sodium. This chilled soup is designed to be gentle on the esophagus, easy to digest, and free from common allergens such as eggs and dairy, with options to substitute oromit potential triggers.

Nutritional Information (per serving, with coconut milk):

- Calories: ~250-300
- Protein: 3-4g
- Total Fat: 20-24g
- Fiber: 7-10g
- Sodium: Low

Quinoa Spinach Frittata with Dairy-Free Option

Serves: 1

Cooking Time: 25 minutes

Ingredients and Portions/Measurements:

- Quinoa: 1/4 cup, cooked (A complete protein source, rich in fiber, supports digestive health)
- Spinach: 1/2 cup, fresh or frozen (Iron and magnesium source, Phase 3 maintenance EOE diet friendly)
- Eggs: 2 large (High in protein and vitamins D, B6, and B12)
- Substitution (if eggs trigger): 1/2 cup chickpea flour mixed with 1/2 cup water (for binding and protein)
- Almond Milk: 1/4 cup (For mixing with eggs or chickpea flour; adds creaminess without dairy)
- Substitution (if almond milk triggers): Oat milk 1/4 cup
- Olive Oil: 1 teaspoon (For sautéing; healthy fat source)
- Nutritional Yeast: 1 tablespoon (Adds a cheesy flavor without dairy; rich in B-vitamins)

- Substitution (if nutritional yeast triggers): A pinch of turmeric for color and anti-inflammatory properties
- Cherry Tomatoes: 1/4 cup, halved (Rich in vitamins C and K, and lycopene)
- Salt and Pepper: To taste

Instructions:

- Prep Quinoa: Start with cooked quinoa. If you haven't already, cook quinoa according to package instructions and let it cool.
- Sauté Spinach: Heat olive oil in a non-stick skillet over medium heat. Add spinach and sauté until wilted. Add cherry tomatoes for the last minute.
- Mix Eggs or Substitute: In a bowl, whisk together the eggs (or chickpea flour and water mixture) with almond milk (or oat milk), nutritional yeast (or turmeric), salt, and pepper. Stir in the cooked quinoa.
- Combine: Add the egg mixture to the skillet with the spinach and tomatoes, making sure the ingredients are evenly distributed.
- Cook: Cover the skillet with a lid and cook on a low-medium heat for 10-15 minutes, or until the frittata is firm and cooked through. You can finish it under the broiler for a minute or two for a golden top.

- Serve: Carefully slide the frittata onto a plate. It can be served hot or at room temperature.

Scientific Note:

This recipe provides a balanced meal with a good mix of proteins, healthy fats, and carbohydrates, suitable for the maintenance phase of an EoE diet. The substitutions ensure that individuals who are sensitive to eggs or dairy can still enjoy a nutritious and fulfilling meal without triggering symptoms. Quinoa and spinach offer a high nutrient density, supporting overall health and well-being.

Nutritional Information (per serving, with egg substitution):

- Calories: ~300-350
- Protein: 10-15g
- Total Fat: 15-20g
- Fiber: 3-5g
- Sodium: Low to Moderate

DINNER RECIPES

MAINTENANCE PHASE 3

Baked Sweet Potato and Greens Bowl

Serves: 1

Cooking Time: 45 minutes (mostly for baking the sweet potato)

Ingredients and Portions/Measurements:

- Sweet Potato: 1 medium (Rich in beta-carotene, vitamin C, and fiber)
- Kale or Spinach: 1 cup, chopped (Iron and magnesium source, Phase 3 maintenance EOE diet friendly)
- Chickpeas: 1/2 cup, cooked or canned (Protein and fiber source, substitute for eggs)
- Coconut Milk: 2 tablespoons (For creaminess, substitute for milk)
- Substitution (if coconut milk triggers): Rice milk 2 tablespoons
- Olive Oil: 1 teaspoon (For roasting and sautéing; healthy fat source)

- Paprika: 1/2 teaspoon (For seasoning sweet potato and chickpeas)
- Garlic Powder: 1/4 teaspoon (Optional, based on tolerance)
- Salt and Pepper: To taste

Instructions:

- Bake Sweet Potato: Preheat your oven to 400°F (200°C). Pierce the sweet potato several times with a fork, then wrap it in aluminum foil. Bake in the preheated oven for 35-45 minutes, or until tender.
- Prepare Chickpeas: If using canned chickpeas, rinse and drain them. Toss chickpeas with olive oil, paprika, garlic powder (if using), salt, and pepper. Spread them on a baking sheet and roast in the oven alongside the sweet potato for 20-25 minutes, or until crispy.
- Sauté Greens: Heat a teaspoon of olive oil in a pan over medium heat. Add kale or spinach and sauté until wilted. Season with a pinch of salt and pepper.
- Assemble Bowl: Once the sweet potato is cooked and slightly cooled, cut it open and fluff the inside with a fork. Add the sautéed greens and roasted chickpeas. Drizzle with coconut milk (or rice milk) for creaminess.

- Serve: Enjoy your warm and nutritious Baked Sweet Potato and Greens Bowl.

Scientific Note:

This recipe caters to the needs of those in the maintenance phase of an EoE diet, focusing on whole, minimally processed ingredients. Sweet potatoes provide a rich source of dietary fiber and antioxidants, while chickpeas offer plant-based protein and satiety. Kale or spinach contributes important vitamins and minerals, supporting overall health. The use of coconut or rice milk as a dairy substitute ensures the meal remains inclusive for those with sensitivities, providing a balanced, allergen-friendly dinner option.

Nutritional Information (approximate, per serving):

- Calories: ~400-450
- Protein: 10-12g
- Total Fat: 10-12g
- Fiber: 8-10g
- Sodium: Moderate

Lemon Herb Chicken with Quinoa Salad

Serves: 1

Cooking Time: 30 minutes

Ingredients and Portions/Measurements:

- Chicken Breast: 1 small (about 4-6 ounces, high in protein, Phase 3 maintenance EOE diet friendly)
- Quinoa: 1/4 cup (uncooked) (Rich in fiber and complete protein)
- Lemon Juice: 2 tablespoons (For marinade and dressing, rich in vitamin C)
- Olive Oil: 2 teaspoons (For dressing and sautéing, source of healthy fat)
- Mixed Greens: 1 cup (Spinach, arugula, etc., iron and magnesium source)
- Cherry Tomatoes: 1/4 cup, halved (Vitamin C rich, enhances immune function)
- Cucumber: 1/4 cup, diced (Hydration and fiber)
- Fresh Herbs: 2 tablespoons (parsley and/or dill, for flavor and nutrients)
- Almond Milk Yogurt: 2 tablespoons (Dairy-free, for creaminess in dressing)
- Substitution (if almond milk triggers): Coconut yogurt

- Salt and Pepper: To taste

Instructions:

- Marinate Chicken: In a bowl, combine 1 tablespoon lemon juice, 1 teaspoon olive oil, salt, and pepper. Marinate the chicken breast for at least 15 minutes.
- Cook Quinoa: Rinse quinoa under cold water, then cook according to package instructions. Fluff with a fork and set aside to cool.
- Cook Chicken: Heat a pan over medium heat. Cook the marinated chicken for 5-7 minutes per side, or until fully cooked. Let it rest for a few minutes, then slice.
- Prepare Salad: In a large bowl, combine cooked quinoa, mixed greens, cherry tomatoes, cucumber, and fresh herbs.
- Make Dressing: Whisk together the remaining lemon juice, olive oil, and almond milk yogurt (or substitute) to create a creamy dressing. Season with salt and pepper.
- Assemble: Add the sliced chicken to the salad. Drizzle with the lemon herb dressing.
- Serve: Enjoy your Lemon Herb Chicken with Quinoa Salad, a refreshing and balanced meal.

Scientific Note:

This meal is tailored for those in the maintenance phase of an EoE diet, focusing on lean proteins, whole grains, and fresh vegetables to provide a balanced and nutritious dinner. The almond milk yogurt in the dressing offers a dairy-free alternative to traditional creaminess, making it suitable for those avoiding dairy. Quinoa is a gluten-free grain that's also a complete protein, supporting muscle health and digestive wellness.

Nutritional Information (approximate, per serving):

- Calories: ~400-450
- Protein: 25-30g
- Total Fat: 10-15g
- Fiber: 5-7g
- Sodium: Moderate

Quinoa Stuffed Bell Peppers

Serves: 1

Cooking Time: 50 minutes

Ingredients and Portions/Measurements:

- Bell Pepper: 1 large (Vitamin C rich, supports immune function)
- Quinoa: 1/4 cup, uncooked (Complete protein source, rich in fiber)
- Black Beans: 1/2 cup, cooked or canned (Protein and fiber source, substitute for eggs)
- Tomato: 1/4 cup, diced (Lycopene source, supports heart health)
- Corn: 1/4 cup (Fiber, vitamins, and minerals)
- Cilantro: 2 tablespoons, chopped (Flavor and antioxidants)
- Lime Juice: 1 tablespoon (Vitamin C and freshness)
- Olive Oil: 1 teaspoon (For cooking, source of healthy fats)
- Cumin: 1/2 teaspoon (For flavor)
- Chili Powder: 1/4 teaspoon (For a little heat, adjust to taste)

- Dairy-Free Cheese: 2 tablespoons, shredded (Optional, for topping, substitute for milk-based cheese)
- Substitution (if dairy-free cheese triggers): Nutritional yeast for a cheesy flavor without dairy
- Salt and Pepper: To taste

Instructions:

- Preheat Oven: Preheat your oven to 375°F (190°C).
- Prepare Quinoa: Cook quinoa according to package instructions. Set aside.
- Prepare Bell Pepper: Cut the top off the bell pepper and remove the seeds and membranes. Place in a baking dish.
- Make Filling: In a bowl, mix cooked quinoa, black beans, tomato, corn, half of the cilantro, lime juice, olive oil, cumin, chili powder, salt, and pepper.
- Stuff Bell Pepper: Fill the bell pepper with the quinoa mixture. Top with dairy-free cheese or nutritional yeast if using.
- Bake: Cover with foil and bake for about 30-35 minutes, or until the pepper is tender. Remove the foil in the last 5 minutes to melt the cheese substitute.

- Serve: Garnish with the remaining cilantro. Serve warm.

Scientific Note:

This recipe offers a balanced mix of plant-based protein, complex carbohydrates, and healthy fats, making it ideal for the maintenance phase of an EoE diet. Quinoa and black beans provide a high protein content that's crucial for repair and growth. Bell peppers are an excellent source of vitamin C, which can help repair tissue and enhance immune function. The optional dairy-free cheese or nutritional yeast allows for customization based on individual tolerances and preferences.

Nutritional Information (approximate, per serving):

- Calories: ~350-400
- Protein: 12-15g
- Total Fat: 7-10g
- Fiber: 8-10g
- Sodium: Moderate

Baked Turmeric and Ginger Chicken with Coconut Rice

Serves: 1

Cooking Time: 30 minutes

Ingredients and Portions/Measurements:

- Chicken Breast: 1 piece (Lean protein, high in essential amino acids)
- Ground Turmeric: 1 teaspoon (Anti-inflammatory properties, EoE friendly)
- Ground Ginger: 1 teaspoon (Gastrointestinal soothing, anti-inflammatory)
- Coconut Milk (For Rice): 1/2 cup (Lactose-free, rich in vitamins and minerals)
- Substitution for Coconut Milk: Almond milk (if coconut triggers)
- Basmati Rice: 1/2 cup (Easy to digest, low allergenic potential)
- Broccoli Florets: 1/2 cup (High in fiber and vitamins C and K)
- Olive Oil: 1 teaspoon (For baking, healthy monounsaturated fats)
- Salt and Pepper: To taste

Instructions:

- Preheat Oven: To 375°F (190°C). Line a baking sheet with parchment paper.
- Season Chicken: Rub the chicken breast with turmeric, ginger, salt, and pepper. Place on the prepared baking sheet and drizzle with olive oil.
- Bake Chicken: Place in the oven and bake for 20-25 minutes, or until fully cooked (internal temperature of 165°F or 74°C).
- Cook Rice: While the chicken is baking, rinse basmati rice under cold water. In a pot, bring coconut milk (or almond milk if substituting) and 1/2 cup of water to a boil. Add rice, reduce heat to low, cover, and simmer for 18-20 minutes, or until liquid is absorbed.
- Steam Broccoli: In the last 10 minutes of baking the chicken, add broccoli florets to the baking sheet or steam separately for a softer texture.
- Serve: Fluff the coconut rice onto a plate, top with baked turmeric and ginger chicken, and side with steamed broccoli.

Scientific Note:

This dish combines the healing properties of turmeric and ginger *with the nutritional benefits of lean chicken and* broccoli. *Turmeric contains curcumin, known for its anti-inflammatory effects, which can be beneficial for EoE sufferers by potentially reducing esophageal inflammation. Ginger has been shown to aid digestion and soothe the gastrointestinal tract. Using coconut milk for the rice provides a dairy-free alternative to traditional milk, offering medium-chain triglycerides (MCTs) that are easier on the stomach for those with dairy sensitivities.*

Nutritional Information (approximate, per serving with coconut milk):

- Calories: 400-450
- Protein: 25-30g
- Total Fat: 15-20g
- Fiber: 3-5g
- Sodium: Moderate

Quinoa Veggie Stir-Fry with Tofu

Serves: 1

Cooking Time: 30 minutes

Ingredients and Portions/Measurements:

- Quinoa: 1/2 cup (A complete protein source, rich in fiber, gluten-free)
- Extra Firm Tofu: 1/2 cup, cubed (High in protein; substitution for eggs)
- Almond Milk: 1 tablespoon (For cooking tofu; substitution for milk)
- Carrots: 1/4 cup, thinly sliced (Rich in beta-carotene and fiber)
- Snap Peas: 1/4 cup (Low calorie, provides a crunchy texture)
- Red Bell Pepper: 1/4 cup, sliced (High in vitamin C and antioxidants)
- Soy Sauce (Low Sodium): 1 teaspoon (For flavor; ensure it's gluten-free if necessary)
- Olive Oil: 1 teaspoon (Healthy fat, for stir-frying)
- Garlic: 1 clove, minced (For flavor and health benefits)
- Ginger: 1/2 teaspoon, grated (Aids digestion, adds a warm flavor)

Instructions:

- Prep Tofu: Press tofu to remove excess moisture. Marinate in almond milk for 10 minutes to imbibe a subtle, creamy flavor, mimicking the richness of eggs.
- Cook Quinoa: Rinse quinoa under cold water. In a saucepan, combine quinoa with 1 cup of water. Bring to a boil, then cover, reduce heat, and simmer for 15 minutes or until water is absorbed. Remove from heat and let it sit covered for 5 minutes. Fluff with a fork.
- Stir-Fry Veggies and Tofu: In a pan, heat olive oil over medium heat. Add minced garlic and grated ginger, sautéing for about 1 minute until fragrant. Add tofu cubes, carrots, snap peas, and red bell pepper. Stir-fry for about 5-7 minutes until the vegetables are tender but still crisp. Pour in the soy sauce and stir well.
- Combine: Add cooked quinoa to the pan with vegetables and tofu. Toss everything together over low heat for an additional 2-3 minutes.
- Serve: Plate the quinoa veggie stir-fry. Garnish with fresh herbs if desired.

Scientific Note:

This dish is carefully crafted for those in the maintenance phase of an EoE diet, focusing on foods that are generally well-tolerated while providing essential nutrients. Quinoa is a gluten-free grain that serves as an excellent protein source, making it an ideal base for this meal. Tofu is used as a substitute for eggs, offering a high-protein alternative without the allergenic risks associated with eggs. Almond milk provides a dairy-free option to introduce creaminess to the dish, suitable for those who must avoid cow's milk.

Nutritional Information (approximate, per serving):

- Calories: 400-450
- Protein: 18-22g
- Total Fat: 10-14g
- Fiber: 5-7g
- Sodium: Low to Moderate

7 DAYS MEAL PLAN FOR MAINTENANCE PHASE

Day 1

Breakfast: Sweet Potato and Black Bean Breakfast Burrito

Lunch: Mediterranean Quinoa Salad with Lemon-Tahini Dressing

Dinner: Baked Sweet Potato and Greens Bowl

Day 2

Breakfast: Coconut Rice Porridge with Fruit Compote

Lunch: Cucumber Noodle Salad with Sunflower Seed Dressing

Dinner: Lemon Herb Chicken with Quinoa Salad

Day 3

Breakfast: Savory Oatmeal with Sautéed Vegetables

Lunch: Lemon Herb Quinoa with Grilled Vegetables

Dinner: Quinoa Stuffed Bell Peppers

Day 4

Breakfast: Pumpkin Seed Pesto Zoodles with Poached Chicken

Lunch: Chilled Avocado Soup with Tomato Relish

Dinner: Baked Turmeric and Ginger Chicken with Coconut Rice

Day 5

Breakfast: Pear and Walnut Oat Bran Bowl

Lunch: Quinoa Spinach Frittata with Dairy-Free Option

Dinner: Quinoa Veggie Stir-Fry with Tofu

Day 6

Breakfast: Sweet Potato and Black Bean Breakfast Burrito

Lunch: Mediterranean Quinoa Salad with Lemon-Tahini Dressing

Dinner: Lemon Herb Chicken with Quinoa Salad

Day 7

Breakfast: Coconut Rice Porridge with Fruit Compote

Lunch: Cucumber Noodle Salad with Sunflower Seed Dressing

Dinner: Baked Turmeric and Ginger Chicken with Coconut Rice

MEAL PLANNER

NEGLECT THE SNACKS AND APPETIZER

AMOS JIMMY
DAILY MEAL PLANNER

DATE ————————————   M T W T F S S
:

BREAKFAST

DINNER

LUNCH

NOTES

SNACKS

JIMMY'S CULINARY HAVEN

Jimmy Asking For An Honest Review

I wanted to reach out and personally thank you for taking the time to explore the world of flavors and creations that I poured into those pages.

Your experience matters a lot to me, and I would be truly grateful if you could share your honest thoughts in a review. Whether it's a brief note or a detailed reflection, your feedback will not only help me grow as a creator but also guide fellow food enthusiasts in deciding if this cookbook is a culinary adventure they'd like to embark on.

Feel free to highlight your favorite recipes, share any challenges you conquered, or even suggest what you'd love to see more of in future editions. Your unique perspective adds a special spice to the whole mix!

Thank you again for being a part of this delicious journey. I can't wait to hear what you think!

Made in United States
Orlando, FL
06 October 2024